# Scientific Investigations

## by Elaine Wood and Pam Walker

*illustrated by Janet Armbrust*

*cover illustrations by Don Ellens*

*cover design by Jeff Van Kanegan*

Publisher
Instructional Fair • TS Denison
Grand Rapids, Michigan 49544

ISBN: 1-56822-424-9

*Scientific Investigations*

Copyright © 1997 by Instructional Fair · TS Denison

2400 Turner Avenue NW

Grand Rapids, Michigan 49544

# TABLE OF CONTENTS

**Life Science**

Iodine Is Not Just for Cuts . . . . . . . . . . . . . . . . . . . . . . . . . . . . . . . . . .1

Mapping the Human Tongue . . . . . . . . . . . . . . . . . . . . . . . . . . . . . . .5

Are Two Good Ears Better Than One? . . . . . . . . . . . . . . . . . . . . . . .10

Judging From Your Reaction . . . . . . . . . . . . . . . . . . . . . . . . . . . . . .15

Keying In on Enzymes . . . . . . . . . . . . . . . . . . . . . . . . . . . . . . . . . . .20

Can One Rotten Banana Spoil the Whole Bunch? . . . . . . . . . . . . . .25

A Jammin' Good Indicator . . . . . . . . . . . . . . . . . . . . . . . . . . . . . . .29

If in Doubt, Watch 'Em Sprout! . . . . . . . . . . . . . . . . . . . . . . . . . . . .34

Making a Difference . . . . . . . . . . . . . . . . . . . . . . . . . . . . . . . . . . . .39

Chef for a Day . . . . . . . . . . . . . . . . . . . . . . . . . . . . . . . . . . . . . . . .43

Bacteria in My Food! . . . . . . . . . . . . . . . . . . . . . . . . . . . . . . . . . . .48

It's Alive! or Is It? . . . . . . . . . . . . . . . . . . . . . . . . . . . . . . . . . . . . . .52

**Physical Science**

Any Way You Measure It . . . . . . . . . . . . . . . . . . . . . . . . . . . . . . . . .56

A Dense Situation . . . . . . . . . . . . . . . . . . . . . . . . . . . . . . . . . . . . . .60

Making Atoms and Molecules Crystal Clear . . . . . . . . . . . . . . . . . . .64

Let's Measure Surface Tension . . . . . . . . . . . . . . . . . . . . . . . . . . . . .68

Monument Eaters . . . . . . . . . . . . . . . . . . . . . . . . . . . . . . . . . . . . . .73

Too Hard to Clean . . . . . . . . . . . . . . . . . . . . . . . . . . . . . . . . . . . . .78

Like Dissolves Like . . . . . . . . . . . . . . . . . . . . . . . . . . . . . . . . . . . . .82

Polymer Strength . . . . . . . . . . . . . . . . . . . . . . . . . . . . . . . . . . . . . .87

Geronimo! . . . . . . . . . . . . . . . . . . . . . . . . . . . . . . . . . . . . . . . . . . .92

Pick It Up! . . . . . . . . . . . . . . . . . . . . . . . . . . . . . . . . . . . . . . . . . . .98

A Very Cool Activity . . . . . . . . . . . . . . . . . . . . . . . . . . . . . . . . . . . .103

**Earth Science**

How Far Is a "People Year"? . . . . . . . . . . . . . . . . . . . . . . . . . . . . . .108

Distances and Diameters . . . . . . . . . . . . . . . . . . . . . . . . . . . . . . . .112

Dinosaur Feet . . . . . . . . . . . . . . . . . . . . . . . . . . . . . . . . . . . . . . . .119

It's a Dirty Job But Somebody Has to Do It! . . . . . . . . . . . . . . . . . .124

Moisture in the Soil . . . . . . . . . . . . . . . . . . . . . . . . . . . . . . . . . . . .129

It's Hot in Here . . . . . . . . . . . . . . . . . . . . . . . . . . . . . . . . . . . . . . .133

A Chip Off the Old Block . . . . . . . . . . . . . . . . . . . . . . . . . . . . . . . .137

Summer Breezes . . . . . . . . . . . . . . . . . . . . . . . . . . . . . . . . . . . . . .142

Shake It Up . . . . . . . . . . . . . . . . . . . . . . . . . . . . . . . . . . . . . . . . . .147

**Answer Key** . . . . . . . . . . . . . . . . . . . . . . . . . . . . . . . . . . . . . . . . . .153

# TO THE TEACHER

When students are active in their own learning processes, their work becomes meaningful and they retain concepts presented in class. This book contains science labs that are appealing to students and will engage them as active learners.

The experiments found in *Scientific Investigations* cover the disciplines of life science, physical science, and earth science. The materials required for each lab are easy to acquire and are inexpensive. A teacher page prior to each activity gives in-depth information on the topic, teaching suggestions, amount of time required to complete the activity, and an overview of the activity. The student pages include a "Background" page that explains the concept to the learner. Teachers do not need supplementary material to complete the lab. The lab activity pages include easy-to-follow directions, data tables and charts, and a conclusion section.

The recently published *National Science Education Standards* recommends that middle school science should provide full inquiry and partial inquiry activities for students. *Scientific Investigations* includes both types of inquiry activities. "Geronimo," a fall-inquiry activity, is about parachute construction. In this activity students design an investigation, gather evidence, draw conclusions, and report their findings to the class. The activity, "It's Hot in Here," is about the greenhouse effect and requires students to use partial inquiry skills. The technique of partial inquiry allows students to develop their skills of investigation and use background information and experimental results to arrive at conclusions.

This book is divided into three sections. A list of the topics follows:

## Life Science
- how enzymes work
- taste buds
- reaction time
- acid-base indicators
- variations in the population
- yeast fermentation
- starch indicators
- how we perceive sound
- ethylene and fruit ripening
- seed germination
- food spoilage
- living things and bacteria in food

## Physical Science
- hard/soft water
- strength of polymers
- levers
- density of salt
- separation of mixtures
- effects of acid rain
- the properties and production of soap
- parachute design
- insulation
- models of molecules
- surface tension of water

## Earth Science
- light years
- fossil evidence
- percentage of water in soil types
- erosion and weathering
- the diameter of celestial bodies
- water retention of soils
- the greenhouse effect
- the effect of bodies of water on climate

# IODINE IS NOT JUST FOR CUTS

**Objective:** Students will test their saliva for the presence of an enzyme that changes starch to sugar.

**Time Required:** 20 to 30 minutes

**Notes to the Teacher:**
Starch agar petri plates can be prepared in several ways.

a. Order small petri plates and dry starch agar from science supply houses. Follow the directions on the starch agar box to mix the agar, heat to boiling, and pour into plates. Let plates cool for 30 minutes. Refrigerate plates that you do not plan to use that day.

b. Order starch agar plates that have already been poured.

c. Prepare Knox gelatin, and add two tablespoons of corn starch. Boil, pour in petri plates, saucers, or shallow bowls. Refrigerate overnight.

Designate a container for swab disposal.

Designate a container into which students can pour excess iodine after they flood their plates.

Use reagent grade tincture of iodine, or mix over-the-counter iodine with a little water to dilute. Before the lab, place some iodine on a slice of potato so that students can see the results of a positive iodine test, or place iodine on one of the starch agar plates as a control.

When students flood their plates with iodine, you can expect one of these two results:
a) Initials will appear light in color. The remainder of the plate will appear blue-black. In places where amylase touched the starch agar, starch was changed to sugar. Sugar does not react with iodine. b) The entire plate will appear blue-black. The swabs that touched these plates did not contain amylase, so starch was present on the entire plate.

To extend this activity, have students determine the percentage of classmates with the enzyme for digesting starch in their saliva. Or, if you have enough starch agar plates, let students take them home and have various members of their family swab the agar. Iodine can be added the next day in class. Students could then understand how they inherited the trait for the presence of amylase in their mouths.

# IODINE IS NOT JUST FOR CUTS

When food is digested, complex molecules are changed to simple molecules. Cells in the body can absorb simple molecules and use them to make energy. Sugar is a simple molecule that cells can use.

The digestive system begins in the mouth where food is chewed and mixed with saliva. Some people have in their saliva an enzyme that changes starch, a complex molecule, to sugar, a smaller and simpler molecule. Enzymes are substances that help chemical reactions take place in living things.

Food that has been chewed and mixed with saliva is pushed down the esophagus by the tongue. The esophagus leads to the stomach, a large sack that stores food and produces several digestive chemicals. Some of these chemicals are enzymes that help break down fats and proteins in the stomach. Hydrochloric acid is found there also. This acid kills any dangerous bacteria that might have entered the stomach, and it helps dissolve food.

Partially digested food passes from the stomach to the small intestine. Most digestion occurs in the small intestine. Enzymes that break down all types of food are found there. When food is completely digested into simple molecules, it is absorbed by the bloodstream, which carries it to all the cells of the body.

Iodine is a chemical indicator that changes from a dark red color to purple or black in the presence of starch. Many foods, such as potatoes, bread, and rice, contain starch. A drop of iodine on such foods will turn blue-black. We can use this reaction of starch and iodine to test for the presence of a starch-digesting enzyme in our saliva.

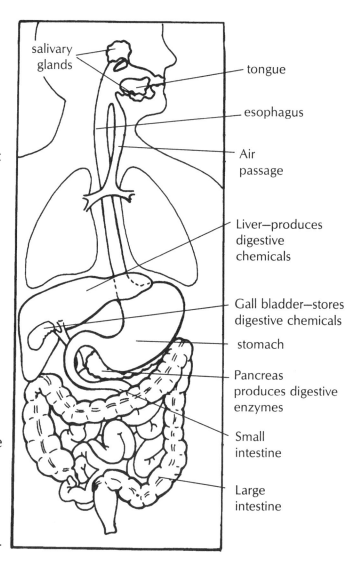

# IODINE IS NOT JUST FOR CUTS

**PURPOSE:** Test your saliva for the presence of an enzyme that changes starch to sugar.

**MATERIALS NEEDED:**
Swab
Petri dish containing starch agar
Iodine
Container for swab disposal
Container for disposal of iodine

**PROCEDURE:**

1. Place one end of a cotton swab in your mouth.

2. Suck on it gently until the swab is saturated with saliva.

3. Partially open the petri dish so that your swab will fit inside. Use the swab to gently write your initials on the starch agar. Dispose of the swab and replace the lid on the petri dish.

   *Caution: Do not exchange used swabs with another student. Follow your teacher's directions for swab disposal.*

4. Wait five minutes; then flood the plate with a few drops of iodine solution.

5. Pour the excess iodine on your plate into a container designated by the teacher.

6. Carefully examine your plate to determine whether or not you can read your initials.

7. Write your name in the correct column in the Data Table.

8. Ask other students in your class whether their saliva contains the starch-digesting enzyme. Place each student's name in the correct column in your Data Table.

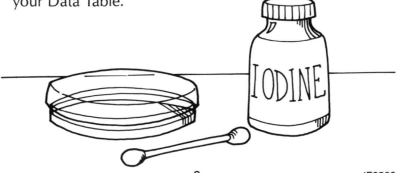

**Data Table:** Class results of survey for the presence of a starch-digesting enzyme in saliva

| Students who have the starch-digesting enzyme | Students who do not have the starch-digesting enzyme |
|---|---|
|  |  |
|  |  |
|  |  |

### CONCLUSIONS:

1. Can you read your initials on the starch agar? (If you cannot, look at a plate with initials.)

   _____

2. Are the initials a light color or a dark color? Why?

   _____

   _____

3. What color is the rest of the starch agar plate? _____

4. If your initials are a light color, do you have the enzyme in your mouth for digesting starch? _____

5. How many students are in your science class today? How many of these have the enzyme in their mouths that breaks down glucose? _____

# MAPPING THE HUMAN TONGUE

**Objective:** Students will determine whether or not some areas of the tongue are more sensitive to particular tastes.

**Time Required:** 40 to 50 minutes

**Notes to the Teacher:**
Instruct students not to guess which substances are being dropped on their tongue if they cannot determine this by their sense of taste. Indicate that the tester must take good notes during this activity so that partners can map areas of the tongue that are sensitive to specific tastes.

Results will vary but generally students should be able to determine that the tip and front sides of the tongue are sensitive to salty tastes, and that the tip and top of the front half are sensitive to sweet tastes. The back sides of the tongue can detect sour and the back of the tongue can detect bitter. The center will not be able to detect any tastes.

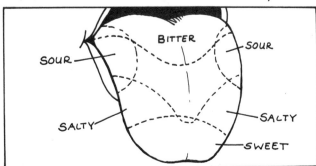

**Figure 1: Areas of the tongue that respond to different tastes**

This activity can be extended by letting students rub ice on their tongues, then repeat their taste tests. They probably will not be able to determine taste as well when their tongues are cold. Taste buds work best when food is between 72° and 105° Fahrenheit (22° and 42° Celsius).

To show students that the senses of smell and taste are linked, grate some apple, potato, and onion. Blindfold students and have them taste a little of each food while holding their noses. Be certain that students take only very small samples, because food texture can help students guess the foods they are tasting.

# MAPPING THE HUMAN TONGUE

Your senses collect information about things around you and send that information to your brain. You have millions of receptors in your skin that can detect touch, temperature, and pain. Additionally, you have four major sense organs: the eyes, ears, tongue, and nose.

Your sense of taste is due to special chemical receptors on your tongue called *papillae*. These bumps are organs that sense basic tastes of sweet, sour, salt, or bitter. Each papilla contains hundreds of cells called "taste buds."

When a sour substance comes in contact with a taste bud sensitive to sour, the nerve cells in that taste bud respond by sending a message to your brain that says "this tastes sour." Taste buds are only responsive to specific flavors. In other words, sour taste buds will not respond to sweet tastes. Likewise, sweet taste buds will not respond to sour substances.

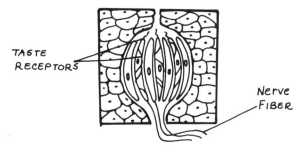

**Figure 1: A taste bud**

All of the flavors that you sense in your food are due to a combination of tastes. As you eat, food made of sweet, sour, salty, and bitter substances passes over your taste buds.

The odor of food also affects how it tastes. When you have congestion and cannot breathe through your nose, your sense of smell does not work as well.

The taste buds are scattered over the surface of the tongue, under the tongue, and on the inside of the cheeks. In this experiment, you will determine whether certain areas of your tongue detect some tastes better than others.

# MAPPING THE HUMAN TONGUE

**PURPOSE:** Determine which areas of the tongue are most sensitive to particular tastes.

**MATERIALS NEEDED:**

| | |
|---|---|
| Sugar | Lemon juice |
| Salt | Vinegar |
| Water | One tablespoon |

Five medicine droppers
Five small paper cups
Two stirring spoons
Cup of water for each student
Masking tape
Blindfold (or just have your partner close his/her eyes)
Paper and pencil

**PROCEDURE:**

1. Working with a partner, place a piece of masking tape on each of the five paper cups.

2. Number the cups 1, 2, 3, 4, and 5.

3. Place the following in the five cups:
   Cup 1—Add ½ cup of water and two teaspoons of sugar and stir.
     This is your sweet solution.
   Cup 2—Add ½ cup of water and two teaspoons of salt and stir.
     This is your salty solution.
   Cup 3—Add ½ cup of vinegar.
     This is your sour solution.
   Cup 4—Add ½ cup of lemon juice.
     This is your bitter solution.
   Cup 5—Fill with water.
     Cup 5 stimulates no taste buds.

4. Place your name under Illustration A of the tongue and your partner's name under Illustration B of the tongue.

5. Each illustration is divided into four sections. These sections indicate the areas on the tongue where you will place a drop of liquid from each cup.

6. Blindfold your partner and ask your partner to pinch his/her nose shut while you are testing.

7. Fill your medicine dropper with liquid from one of the five cups. Do not tell your partner which cup you are using. Ask your partner to stick out his/her tongue. Release one drop of liquid on the location on your partner's tongue that matches section 1 on the illustration.

8. Ask your partner to identify which taste he/she thinks this drop represents. Repeat this test on the same part of the tongue using another solution until all five solutions have been tested on section 1. Take notes on the results.

9. Let your partner rinse his/her mouth with water from cup #5 before the next test.

10. Repeat the steps 7-9 using section 2 of the tongue. Take notes on the results.

11. Repeat steps 7-9 using section 3 of the tongue. Take notes on your results.

12. Repeat steps 7-9 using section 4 of the tongue. Take notes on your results.

13. From your notes you should see a pattern forming. Your partner may be able to detect a taste on a certain area of his/her tongue, but not on other areas. Label which of the four sections seem to indicate salty, bitter, sour, and sweet on Illustration A.

14. If time permits, switch roles with your partner and you do the tasting.

15. Answer the questions in the Conclusions.

**Illustration A—Tongue belonging to _____.**

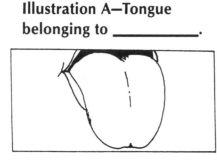

**Illustration B—Tongue belonging to _____.**

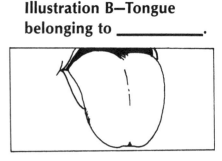

## CONCLUSIONS:

1. Which section of the tongue most accurately identified sweet? _____

2. Which section of the tongue most accurately identified sour? _____

3. Which section of the tongue most accurately identified salty? _____

4. Which section of the tongue most accurately identified bitter? _____

5. What was the purpose of rinsing the mouth with water between tests?

   _____

   _____

   _____

6. Why was it important not to drop the solutions on your partner's tongue in random order?

   _____

   _____

   _____

7. Why did you and your partner hold your noses during the experiment?

   _____

   _____

   _____

 # *ARE TWO GOOD EARS BETTER THAN ONE?*

**Objective:** Students will determine the location from which a sound originates using one ear and then using both ears.

**Time Required:** A 50-minute class period

**Notes to the Teacher:**
To prepare for this activity, push the desks or tables against the classroom walls. Place a chair in the very center of the room. This is where the blindfolded subject will be seated.

Mark off eight places on the floor around the chair so these eight numbers form a square. A simple way of doing this is to place the numbers 1 through 8 on separate sheets of white paper and tape them to the floor in the proper locations. See the diagram on the student procedure page.

Select eight students to participate as "bouncers." Select one student to sit blindfolded in the center of the room. Ask bouncers to stand behind one of the eight numbers on the floor. The remaining students, the "recorders," will sit in the desks around the wall. These students will record the results from the first round of testing.

After all students have assumed their positions and the subject is blindfolded, write a number between 1–8 on the chalkboard. The person standing behind this number should bounce his/her basketball one time on the floor. The blindfolded subject will point in the direction from which the sound came. Recorders will enter these results in Table 1. Repeat this process a total of 16 times. Each time, write a different number on the board.

After the first 16 trials, give the subject an earplug to place in one ear. Repeat the process described above for 16 more times with the same group. Recorders will enter these results in Table 2.

If time permits, have the recorders, bouncers, and the blindfolded subject switch roles and repeat the lab.

# ARE TWO GOOD EARS BETTER THAN ONE?

Sense organs help provide information to animals about what is happening all around them. Ears are sense organs that interpret sounds. Sound results from vibrations moving through materials such as air, water, and earth. When these vibrations reach ears, the ears and brain interpret them as sound.

Some animals have large, moveable ears. Visualize the big ears of jack rabbits and bats. A jack rabbit's keen sense of hearing enables it to scurry away from predators. Bats have natural radar; they emit high-pitched sounds, then listen for the echoes of these sounds. Human ears are small in comparison to those of several animals. Many scientists believe that humans have small ears because they primarily rely on their sense of vision.

There is much more to the ear than the part you can see. The outer ear opens into a canal that leads to the eardrum. Vibrations travel down the canal and cause the eardrum to vibrate. The vibrations of the eardrum are transmitted to bones of the middle ear. These bones relay the vibrations to the snail-shaped *cochlea* of the inner ear. Fluid in the cochlea vibrates, and these vibrations are picked up by cells in this structure. These cells send nerve signals to the brain. The brain interprets these vibrations as sound (see Figure 1).

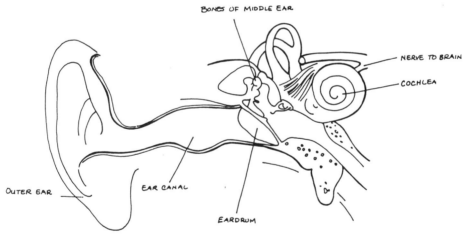

**Figure 1: Ear and nerves to the brain**

Blind people rely on their sense of hearing much more than people who can see. Even though a blind person cannot see someone enter the room, he or she can detect the direction from which sounds are created. To determine the direction from which a sound is produced, a person must have two ears.

A vibration traveling toward you arrives at one of your ears a split second sooner than it arrives at the other ear. The sound is a little louder in the ear that received it first. The brain uses the time difference and the difference in loudness to determine the location of the sound.

# ARE TWO GOOD EARS BETTER THAN ONE?

**PURPOSE:** Determine the origin of sounds by using one ear and then by using both ears.

**MATERIALS NEEDED:**
> Pencil and paper
> Eight basketballs, soccer balls, or volleyballs
> Chalkboard
> Blindfold
> Chair
> Earplug

**PROCEDURE:**

1. Eight "bouncers" take a ball and go to one of the eight bouncer positions.

    The blindfolded subject sits in a chair in the center of the room.

    Recorders sit in desks and write down the results of the experiment. At the end of the first test, subject, recorders, and bouncers will trade jobs.

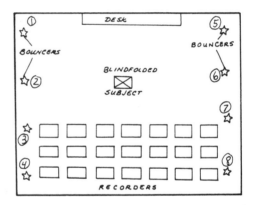

**Figure 2: Diagram of the room**

2. The teacher will write a number on the chalkboard. The bouncer who is standing at the position that corresponds to the number on the chalkboard will bounce his/her basketball one time. The blindfolded subject will point to the direction from which he/she believes the sound came.

3. In Table 1, recorders will write a (+) for correct responses and a (−) for incorrect responses by the subject.

4. The teacher will write another number on the board and the procedure will be repeated. Continue in this fashion until the blindfolded subject has heard the ball bounce 16 times.

6. After 16 trials, recorders total their results in Table 1.

7. Repeat steps 3, 4, and 5 using the same participants. However, this time the blindfolded subject will wear an earplug in one ear.

8. Record the results of the repeated trials in Table 2.

9. The subject, recorders, and bouncers can trade places and repeat the entire activity.

10. Answer the Conclusion questions.

### Table 1. Determining the Location of Sound Using Two Ears

| Trial Number | Correct Responses (+) | Incorrect Responses (-) |
|---|---|---|
| 1 | | |
| 2 | | |
| 3 | | |
| 4 | | |
| 5 | | |
| 6 | | |
| 7 | | |
| 8 | | |
| 9 | | |
| 10 | | |
| 11 | | |
| 12 | | |
| 13 | | |
| 14 | | |
| 15 | | |
| 16 | | |
| | | |

### Table 2. Determining the Location of Sound Using One Ear

| Trial Number | Correct Responses (+) | Incorrect Responses (-) |
|---|---|---|
| 1 | | |
| 2 | | |
| 3 | | |
| 4 | | |
| 5 | | |
| 6 | | |
| 7 | | |
| 8 | | |
| 9 | | |
| 10 | | |
| 11 | | |
| 12 | | |
| 13 | | |
| 14 | | |
| 15 | | |
| 16 | | |
| | | |

## CONCLUSIONS:

1. When were subjects better able to determine the origin of sound: when they used one ear or two? _____

2. Describe how a blind person might rely on their ears to determine the location of an approaching object or person.

   _____

   _____

   _____

3. Describe the path of sound vibrations through the ear.

   _____

   _____

   _____

4. What is the role of the brain in hearing?

   _____

   _____

   _____

5. If the section of brain that is responsible for hearing is damaged, could one hear?

   _____

   _____

   _____

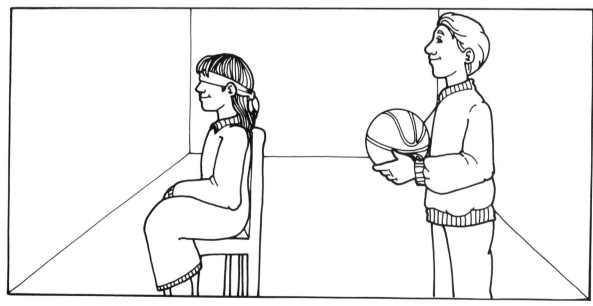

# JUDGING FROM YOUR REACTION . . .

**Objective:** Students will determine their reaction time under different circumstances.

**Time Required:** 50 minutes

**Notes to the Teacher:**
Stress to students that everyone will have different reaction times. There is no correct time in which people respond to events. Remind students that the purpose of establishing a reaction rating in Table 1 is to give them some base line data by which to interpret the results of Tables 2 and 3. Tables 2 and 3 evaluate the effects of distractors on reaction time.

Overall, you can expect student reaction ratings on Tables 2 and 3 to be lower than those on Table 1. Some students may not get the expected results because they are aware of what they are trying to accomplish. Explain that in real life people are not always aware of what is about to happen.

Since students participating in this activity are not yet driving cars, discuss with them the importance of concentrating on the road while driving. Explain that many accidents occur because people are tuning their radios, looking for gum, talking on their cellular phones, etc. To be safe, drivers must concentrate on the road.

Before students begin this lab, they need to prepare their meter sticks. Have them place four pieces of masking tape at the 20 cm, 40 cm, 60 cm, and 80 cm marks. They will use this meter stick to measure their reaction times (see Figure 1).

**Figure 1: The meter stick prepared for rating scales**

| 20 cm | 40 cm | 60 cm | 80 cm |

# JUDGING FROM YOUR REACTION . . .

It takes about one half of a second for you to say the word *science* out loud. It also takes about one half of a second for a major league pitcher's fast ball to travel from his hand to the catcher's mitt. If you are a major league batter, you must react quickly to make contact with the ball. In baseball and other sports, reaction time is important. In everyday events, reaction time is equally important. You do not always know when something is going to happen. Many times, you must be ready and alert for anything.

Let's look at an example when reaction is very important. A car is traveling down a busy street, and a young child runs across the street in front of the car. The driver reacts by slamming on the brakes and swerving to miss the child. The reaction time in this example is the time it takes for the driver to touch the brakes and turn the steering wheel once he/she first sees the child crossing the street.

What happens between the time the driver sees the child and applies his foot to the brake pedal? The driver's eyes detect the movement of the child. Nerve impulses are sent along special nerve cells to the brain. The brain interprets the message it receives in impulses from the eyes. The brain sends a message down the spinal cord to motor *neurons*. These motor neurons transmit the brain's message to muscles in the leg and arms (see Figure 1). This causes the driver to slam on brakes and turn the steering wheel. The time it takes for these impulses to make the complete trip from the eye to the legs and arms is called the *reaction time*.

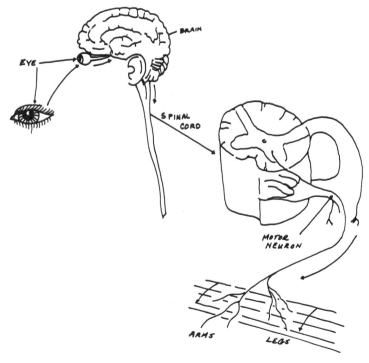

**Figure 1:** A nerve impulse travels from the eye to the brain. The brain interprets the information and sends an impulse to motor neurons in the legs and arms.

What if this driver is thinking about a big project at school or work? What if this driver is looking down at the radio, or talking on his/her cellular phone when the child darts into the street? In other words, what if his/her concentration is not solely on driving? In this lab, you will determine some factors that affect reaction time.

# JUDGING FROM YOUR REACTION . . .

**PURPOSE:** Determine your reaction time under different circumstances.

**MATERIALS NEEDED:**
Pencil and paper
Meter stick
Masking tape

**PROCEDURE:**

1. Wrap a piece of masking tape at the following locations on your meter stick.
   a. 20 cm
   b. 40 cm
   c. 60 cm
   d. 80 cm

2. Write the following words at these locations.
   a. Super
   b. Excellent
   c. Good
   d. Fair

3. Rest your forearm on the surface of your desk. Extend your hand over the edge of the desk so that your thumb and fingers are apart.

4. Have your partner stand beside you and position the meter stick with the zero end between, but not touching, your thumb and fingers (see Figure 1).

5. As soon as your partner releases the meter stick, try to catch it.

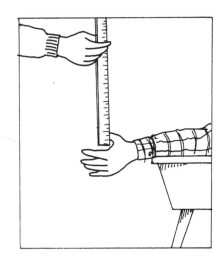

**Figure 1: With your forearm extended over your desk, your partner holds the meter stick between your thumb and fingers.**

6. If you caught the meter stick between the 1 and 20 cm mark, your reaction was Super. If you caught it between the 20 and 40 cm mark, your reaction was Excellent. A catch between the 40 and 60 cm mark is Good. A catch between the 60 and 80 cm mark is Fair. A catch after 80 or a complete miss is Poor. Record your catch ranking in Table 1.

7. Repeat steps 3–6 ten times. Record your rankings each time.

8. Repeat steps 3–6, while reciting the multiplication tables for eight. Example: 1 x 8 = 8, 2 x 8 = 16, etc.

9. Record the ranking you achieved in Table 2.

10. Repeat steps 3–6 with your head turned to the right so that you only see the meter stick in your peripheral vision.

11. Record the ranking you achieved when you caught the meter stick using only your peripheral vision in Table 3.

12. Switch places with your partner and repeat this activity.

### Table 1: Reaction Time—While Concentrating

| Trial # | 1 | 2 | 3 | 4 | 5 | 6 | 7 | 8 | 9 | 10 |
|---|---|---|---|---|---|---|---|---|---|---|
| Partner 1 | | | | | | | | | | |
| Partner 2 | | | | | | | | | | |

### Table 2: Reaction Time—While Reciting Multiplication Tables

| Trial # | 1 | 2 | 3 | 4 | 5 | 6 | 7 | 8 | 9 | 10 |
|---|---|---|---|---|---|---|---|---|---|---|
| Partner 1 | | | | | | | | | | |
| Partner 2 | | | | | | | | | | |

### Table 3: Reaction Time—Using Peripheral Vision

| Trial # | 1 | 2 | 3 | 4 | 5 | 6 | 7 | 8 | 9 | 10 |
|---|---|---|---|---|---|---|---|---|---|---|
| Partner 1 | | | | | | | | | | |
| Partner 2 | | | | | | | | | | |

**CONCLUSIONS:**

1. What effect did reciting your multiplication tables have on your ability to catch the ruler? One day soon you will be driving a car. If you are driving and concentrating on something else, how might this affect your ability to react to an unexpected event?

   _____

   _____

   _____

2. What effect did using your peripheral vision have on your ability to catch the ruler? If you are driving a car, but not looking directly at the road, how might this affect your reaction time to an unexpected event?

   _____

   _____

   _____

3. Describe the path of nerve impulses as they travel from your eye, when you saw the meter stick fall, to your hand when you caught the meter stick.

   _____

   _____

   _____

4. List some other factors that you think might slow one's reaction time while driving a car.

   _____

   _____

   _____

# KEYING IN ON ENZYMES

**Objectives:** Observe evidence of the action of an enzyme on a substance.
Determine the effect of high temperature on enzyme activity.

**Time Required:** 50 minutes

**Notes to the Teacher:**
Set up a hot water bath at the beginning of the period for all students to use. Have them remove pieces of liver after five minutes of boiling. Allow the liver to cool before placing it in the specified test tubes.

Discuss the background section with students prior to the lab. You may choose to mention that meat tenderizer contains an enzyme that makes the surface of meat tender. Discussion of how enzymes can cause browning of fruit is helpful to students in understanding the action of enzymes. Reinforce the fact that after a slaughtered animal is dead or after a crop is harvested, the enzymes in these products may remain active for several weeks if these products are refrigerated.

Review the lock-and-key explanation of an enzyme. Describe for students how enzymes may change in shape as a result of certain conditions. Draw Figure 1 on the chalkboard to show how enzymes can be altered due to changes in temperature and pH. These changed enzymes are like keys that are bent. They will no longer fit their specific locks.

**Figure 1: Enzymes and the substance they affect are like a lock and key. Changes in temperature and pH can alter the shape of the enzyme and interfere with its function.**

Demonstrate how a certain enzyme in liver and many other tissues breaks down hydrogen peroxide to harmless oxygen and water.

$$2H_2O_2 \longrightarrow 2 H_2O + O_2$$

Hydrogen peroxide　　　　　　yields　　　　　water +　　oxygen

Answers in the Data Table will vary but should show a significant change in temperature in test tube 3. Temperature change is evidence of a chemical reaction.

# KEYING IN ON ENZYMES

Enzymes are special types of proteins. These special proteins are involved in many chemical reactions in the body. *Enzymes* are involved in both breaking down and putting together compounds. Living cells contain hundreds of enzymes. The lab you will perform today uses an enzyme found in liver. Although this liver is dead tissue, the enzymes are still functional. Enzymes can remain active for several weeks after the death of a cell.

An enzyme is a type of *catalyst*. A catalyst is any substance that helps a chemical reaction occur. Although catalysts are involved in chemical reactions, they are never destroyed or changed during the reaction. Catalysts are then available to be used in other reactions.

Not all enzymes are the same. Each enzyme has only one specific function. Even though millions of chemical reactions are occurring in the body, each enzyme influences only one specific reaction. Think of the chemical reaction and its enzyme as a lock and key. The enzyme is the key and the substance on which the enzyme acts is the lock. Only one particular key can open that lock (see Figure 1).

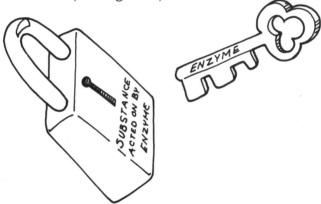

**Figure 1: The action of enzymes on substances can be compared to a lock and key. An enzyme represents the one key that can act on a substance, its specific lock.**

In the body, enzymes also change poisonous chemicals into harmless ones. Without the activity of the enzymes, these chemicals could poison and kill cells. Hydrogen peroxide is a poisonous chemical that is produced in cells. This chemical can be broken down into water and oxygen. Like many chemical reactions, this process is accompanied by the production of heat.

The activity of an enzyme is dependent on several factors, such as pH and temperature. If an enzyme is exposed to a pH or temperature out of its normal range, the shape of the enzyme may change. A change in enzyme shape destroys that enzyme's ability to function. At this point, the key (the enzyme) may no longer fit its lock (the substance it acts upon).

# KEYING IN ON ENZYMES

**PURPOSE:** Determine how enzymes function in living tissue.

Investigate how changes in temperature affect enzyme activity.

**MATERIALS NEEDED:**
Liver (beef or chicken)
Hydrogen peroxide (3% solution)
Thermometer
Six test tubes
Stirring rod
Test tube rack
Grease pencil
Beaker (250 ml)
Scissors
Paper towels
Water
Hot water bath prepared by teacher
Test tube holders

**PROCEDURE:**

1. Place two pieces of liver, both the size of a pea, in a test tube. Fill the test tube about one-half full with water.

2. Place your test tube in the hot water bath your teacher has prepared.

3. Use a grease pencil to number the remaining five test tubes 1 through 5. Place these in order in a test tube rack.

4. Fill test tubes 1, 2, and 4 one-half full of water.

5. Fill test tubes 3 and 5 one-half full of hydrogen peroxide.

6. Use your thermometer to find the temperature of each of the five test tubes. Record the temperature of each test tube under "Starting Temperature" in the Data Table.

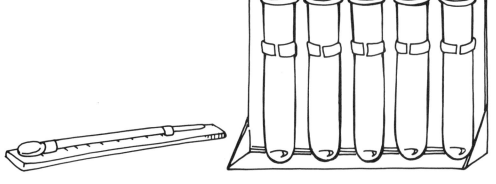

7. One at a time, add the following to the test tubes:

    a. Add nothing to test tube 1.
    b. Place a piece of liver about the size of the end of a pencil eraser in test tube 2. Observe and describe the reaction. After about 30 seconds take the temperature of this test tube. Record the temperature in the Data Table.
    c. Repeat b for test tube 3.

8. Remove the test tube of liver from the water bath using your test tube holder. Carefully pour the hot water in the sink. Pour the pieces of cooked liver on a paper towel.

9. Place one piece of the cooked liver in test tube 4. Observe and describe the reaction. After about 30 seconds, take the temperature inside this test tube. Record the temperature in the Data Table.

10. Place the other piece of cooked liver in test tube 5. Observe and record the reaction in the Data Table. After 30 seconds, take the temperature and record it in the Data Table.

11. Dispose of the contents of your test tubes according to the directions of your teacher.

## Data Table: Enzyme activity in five test tubes

|  | Test tube 1 | Test tube 2 | Test tube 3 | Test tube 4 | Test tube 5 |
|---|---|---|---|---|---|
| Description of reaction |  |  |  |  |  |
| Starting temperature |  |  |  |  |  |
| Temperature after 30 sec. |  |  |  |  |  |

## CONCLUSIONS:

1. In which test tubes were chemical reactions occurring? _____ How do you know?

   _____

2. What was the purpose of test tube 1 in this experiment?

   _____

   _____

3. What effect did cooking the liver have on the activity of the enzyme in hydrogen peroxide? Support your answer.

   _____

   _____

4. The liver in test tubes 4 and 5 was changed. How did cooking the liver affect the "lock-and-key" mechanism of the enzyme?

   _____

   _____

5. Define *enzyme* in your own words.

   _____

   _____

6. Explain why it is important in the body for enzymes to function to break down hydrogen peroxide.

   _____

   _____

7. Explain the reactions you saw in test tubes 2 and 4.

   _____

   _____

8. The liver that was used in the lab was dead. Why did the enzymes in its tissues still function?

   _____

   _____

# CAN ONE ROTTEN BANANA SPOIL THE WHOLE BUNCH?

**Objective:** Determine the conditions necessary for the ripening of fruit.

**Time Required:** About 20 to 30 minutes will be required to set up the lab on Day 1. Thirty or forty minutes will be required on Day 6 to observe the results and complete the lab questions.

**Notes to the Teacher:**

Bananas are the fruit of choice for this activity. You could substitute apples, lemons, or oranges if you prefer. These fruits also produce ethylene which speeds the ripening of unripe fruits.

Discuss the background information with students prior to the lab. You may need to explain the functions of hormones. Review the products of cellular respiration.

In this activity, the paper bags will permit the passage of oxygen. The addition of oxygen speeds up the ripening process. These bags do not allow ethylene produced during ripening to escape. The plastic bags do not allow oxygen to penetrate the bags. The fruit in these bags will not ripen as quickly in the absence of oxygen.

The presence of ethylene in the paper bag and plastic bag with the ripened banana will cause the other banana to ripen faster than normal. The green bananas in the paper bag will ripen more quickly than the green bananas in the plastic bags. The green banana in the paper bag with the ripe banana will ripen the fastest of all bags. The green bananas in the plastic bag will ripen the slowest.

If your results are not conclusive enough after five days, close the bags and allow the experiment to continue for two or three more days.

You may want to discuss with students at the conclusion of the lab, that one rotten banana may spoil the whole bunch.

# CAN ONE ROTTEN BANANA SPOIL THE WHOLE BUNCH?

Which would you rather eat: a green banana, a yellow banana, or a dark brown banana? Most of you would select a yellow banana because it is ripe, but not too ripe. Bananas turn brown as they continue to ripen and eventually spoil.

Where does a green banana get its color, and how does it change colors? Green bananas contain the green pigment, *chlorophyll*. As the banana ripens, this pigment is broken down chemically. Eventually, as the green pigment declines, the yellow pigments, *carotenes* and *flavones,* turn the banana yellow. As fruit ripens, the flesh of the fruit also changes. Chemical changes in the flesh of the fruit change the stiff, bitter fruit into a soft, sweet-tasting food.

Ripening fruit takes in oxygen and releases carbon dioxide. The ripening fruit is actually respiring or breathing. Oxygen is essential for the ripening process. Besides carbon dioxide, another gas is given off during the ripening process. This gas is the hormone, *ethylene.* Remember, a hormone is a chemical messenger. Hormones are produced by cells in one part of the body, and they cause changes in other parts. Ethylene is produced as ripened fruit respires. This hormone also stimulates other pieces of fruit around it to ripen quickly.

In this activity, you will determine the effects that different environmental factors have on the ability of fruit to ripen. Paper bags and plastic bags will be used as containers. Paper bags have small pores in them that allow oxygen to pass through. Plastic bags do not allow the passage of oxygen. Both plastic bags and paper bags do not permit gases, such as ethylene, to escape.

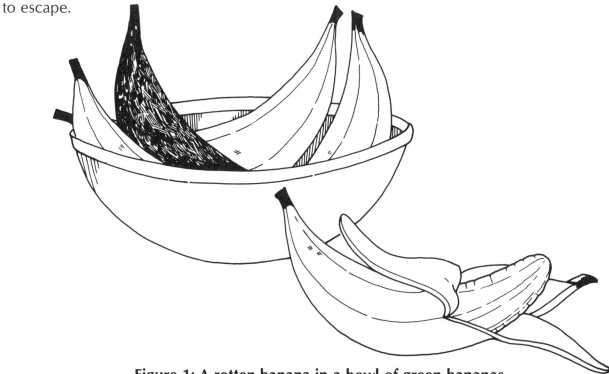

**Figure 1: A rotten banana in a bowl of green bananas**

# CAN ONE ROTTEN BANANA SPOIL THE WHOLE BUNCH?

**PURPOSE:** Determine the conditions necessary for the ripening of fruit.

**MATERIALS NEEDED:**
Two lunch-sized paper bags
Two Zip-loc plastic bags
Six green bananas
Two very ripe bananas
Colored marker
Two clothespins

**PROCEDURE:**

1. Use your colored marker to label the two paper bags, A and B, and the two plastic bags, C and D.

2. Place two green bananas in Bag A. Fold the top of the bag and secure it with a clothespin.

3. Place one very ripe banana and one green banana in Bag B. Fold the top of the bag and secure it with a clothespin.

4. Place two green bananas in Bag C. Use the Zip-loc top to seal the bag shut.

5. Place one very ripe banana and one green banana in Bag D. Close the plastic bag with the Zip-loc seal (see Figure 1).

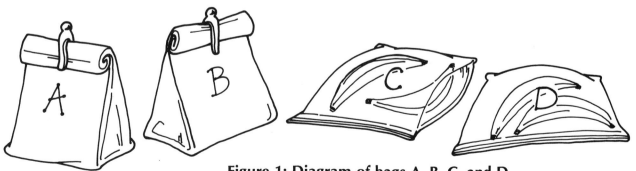

**Figure 1: Diagram of bags A, B, C, and D**

6. Place the bananas in an area of the room where they will not be disturbed for at least five days.

7. At the end of the five-day period, open the four bags and observe the contents.

8. Answer the questions in the Conclusions.

## CONCLUSIONS:

1. Describe the appearance of the bananas in each bag.

Bag A _____

Bag B _____

Bag C _____

Bag D _____

2. Did the presence of a ripe banana in Bag B or D have an effect on the green bananas in those bags? Explain your reasoning.

_____

_____

3. Is oxygen important to the ripening of fruit? Explain how the lab proved this point.

_____

_____

4. If you were a store owner and wanted to keep your fruit fresh for as long as possible, would you wrap your fruit in paper or in plastic? Explain your reason.

_____

_____

5. Define *ethylene*. Why is it called the ripening hormone?

_____

_____

# A JAMMIN' GOOD INDICATOR

**Objective:** Develop and use an acid-base indicator to test the pH of household substances.

**Time Required:** Part A—50 minutes
Part B—30 to 40 minutes

**Notes to the Teacher:**
On Day 1, students will prepare their indicator strips. Hot water is needed. If you do not have hot water in your room, you may want to heat some for the class on a hot plate before lab begins.

After all students have cut and dyed their papers, have them place the papers in a safe location in the room until the next day.

Before class begins on Day 2, set up the unknown household substances in beakers labeled 1–10. Some suggestions for unknowns include the following:

   #1—vinegar
   #2—ammonia
   #3—soap in water
   #4—baking soda in water
   #5—orange juice
   #6—lemon juice
   #7—milk
   #8—a cola drink
   #9—aspirin dissolved in water
   #10—Alka Seltzer dissolved in water

You can use whatever substances you have available at school if you do not have all of the substances listed above.

Place these beakers in the front of the room on Day 2. Students will use their test strips to determine the pH of each sample. Once students have determined and recorded the findings in the Data Table, check the results in their Data Table. Afterwards, reveal the identity of each substance. Have students answer the questions in the Conclusions.

# *A Jammin' Good Indicator*

A substance in a solution that changes its color when added to either an acid or a base is called an *indicator*. Many dyes can be used as indicators. Red cabbage can be shredded and boiled to form a dark blue dye. Remove the cabbage after boiling, keep the liquid, and use it as an indicator. When this liquid is exposed to an acid, it changes to a red color; when exposed to a base, it turns blue.

Indicators can change to a variety of colors depending on the dye used. Bromthymol blue is another indicator. This deep blue solution is only blue when exposed to bases; it turns yellow when exposed to acids. One of the most common indicators in a lab is litmus paper. The dye in litmus papers is made from lichens. Lichens are a combination of a green plant and a fungus. Blue litmus paper remains blue in a base and changes to red in the presence of an acid. Pink litmus paper remains pink in the presence of an acid but turns blue in a base.

What is the difference between an acid and a base? An *acid* is a class of compounds in which water solutions taste sour, turn blue litmus to red, and react with bases to form salts. Think about the sour taste of a grapefruit. Grapefruit juice is an acid. A *base* is a class of compounds that taste bitter, feel slippery in water, turn red litmus blue, and react with acids to form salts. If you have ever gotten soap in your mouth accidentally, you may remember its bitter flavor. Soap is a base.

In this activity, you will make your own indicator from blackberry jelly. This jelly dissolved in water is an excellent indicator. Strips of paper dipped in the solution and dried can be used as indicator strips. When these strips are exposed to an acid, they become red. When exposed to a base, they take on a greenish-purple color.

**Figure 1: Blackberry jelly and indicator strips**

# *A Jammin' Good Indicator*

**PURPOSE:** Develop and use an acid-base indicator to test the pH of household substances.

**MATERIALS NEEDED:**
Blackberry jam
One 500 ml beaker
Hot tap water
Tablespoon
White paper towels
Scissors
Samples to be tested (provided by your teacher)
Microwave-proof plate or a baking rack
Tweezers or forceps

**PROCEDURE:** **Part A**

1. With scissors, cut a piece of white paper towel into strips about 7 centimeters long and 2 centimeters wide. Cut out as many strips as possible from one section of paper towel. Place the strips to the side for later use.

2. Place 250 ml of hot water in your beaker.

3. Add a tablespoonful of blackberry jam to the beaker of water.

4. Stir with your spoon to dissolve the jam in water. Once the jam is dissolved, you are ready to prepare your indicator papers.

5. Using tweezers, dip the strips one at a time in the water and blackberry jam. Let the excess water and jam drip from each strip. If you are using a microwave, place the strips of paper on a microwaveable plate. If you are using a baking rack for an oven, line the baking rack with aluminum foil and place the strips on the baking rack.

6. Microwave your paper strips for 15 seconds, or bake them in an oven at 450°F for 5 to 10 minutes.

7. Remove the strips from the heating unit and repeat steps 6 and 7 until the strips become a darker red. Once the strips are dark, you are ready to conduct your testing.

**Part B**

8. Dip one indicator strip in the unknown substances provided by your teacher. The indicator strips will be red when dipped in an acid and will become greenish-purple in a base.

9. In the Data Table, record the color of each strip after being exposed to an unknown substance. Also indicate whether each substance is an acid or a base.

**Data Table**

| Number of Unknown | Color of strip after exposure to unknown | Acid or Base |
|---|---|---|
| 1 | | |
| 2 | | |
| 3 | | |
| 4 | | |
| 5 | | |
| 6 | | |
| 7 | | |
| 8 | | |
| 9 | | |
| 10 | | |

**CONCLUSIONS:**

1. Define *indicator*. _____

   _____

2. Based on what you learned, predict whether the following substances are acids or bases. Give a reason for your predictions.

   a. Pineapple juice _____

      _____

   b. Tomato juice _____

      _____

   c. Washing powder _____

      _____

   d. Toothpaste _____

      _____

   e. Yogurt_____

      _____

3. Define *acid*. _____

   _____

4. Define *base*._____

   _____

5. Describe the similarity between litmus paper and the indicator strips you prepared today.

   _____

   _____

# IF IN DOUBT, WATCH 'EM SPROUT!

**Objective:** Determine the conditions necessary for the germination of bean seeds.

**Time Required:** Day 1—30 to 40 minutes
Days 2 and 3—10 minutes
Day 4—20 minutes

**Notes to the Teacher:**
Obtain some bean seeds from a local garden center or seed store. You will also need enough paper cups so that each group can have five cups.

Review the term *cotyledon* prior to the lab. Describe to students how a germinating bean seed looks.

The day of the lab, either make arrangements to use a refrigerator or get a cooler of ice to use over the next three days. You will need to check the ice daily to see that it has not melted. Be certain that water does not seep into the cups of seeds placed in the ice.

Check the setup of each group to be certain the conditions have been correctly represented. You may choose to discuss what the five setups represent:

Cup 1—Seeds deprived of water at room temperature
Cup 2—Seeds that are watered at room temperature
Cup 3—Seeds that are watered at cold temperature
Cup 4—Seeds that are watered in room temperature and shielded from light
Cup 5—Seeds that are watered at room temperature but deprived of oxygen

The Data Table may vary from group to group but should show that seeds fail to germinate when deprived of oxygen, water, and warm temperatures.

# IF IN DOUBT, WATCH 'EM SPROUT!

What conditions are necessary for a seed to germinate? *Germination* is the process in which a seed sprouts and produces a new plant. When germination is complete, a young plant called a *seedling* is formed.

For germination to occur, seeds must be *viable*. A viable seed is one which has the ability to produce a plant. Seeds that are not viable will never germinate. During the process of germination, a seed takes up water through its seed coat. The intake of water makes the seed swell. This causes the seed coat to split and allows the young plant to sprout.

When a bean seedling emerges from the soil, it is shaped like a hook. The shoot is bent back to protect its fragile tip as the soil is pushed away.

How do the plants contained in the seeds get food? If you look at a bean seed, you are looking at two halves called *cotyledons.* The food in a cotyledon is in the form of starch. The starch is changed into sugar and sent to the roots and shoots so growth can occur (see Figure 1).

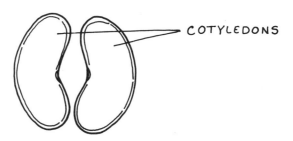

**Figure 1: Two cotyledons of a bean seed**

Viable seeds germinate and grow by receiving nourishment from the cotyledon. What other factors contribute to their growth?

In this activity you will determine what conditions are necessary for germination. The conditions which will be considered include light, water, oxygen, and temperature.

# IF IN DOUBT, WATCH 'EM SPROUT!

**PURPOSE:** Determine the conditions necessary for the germination of bean seeds.

**MATERIALS NEEDED:**

Five small paper cups
Fifteen viable bean seeds
Potting soil
One black piece of felt (large enough to drape over one cup)
Refrigerator, ice chest, or thermos
Masking tape
Pen
Cotton balls
Petroleum jelly
Plastic wrap

**PROCEDURE:**

1. Add potting soil to the five cups so that each is about one-half full of potting soil.

2. Plant three bean seeds in each cup at a depth equal to the length of the seeds. Space seeds around the edge of the cup.

3. Label the cups 1, 2, 3, 4, and 5.

4. Add the following:
   Cup 1—Do not add anything to Cup A during the experiment.
   Cup 2—Add water until the soil is damp. Do not soak the soil in water. Water this cup each day for the next two days.
   Cup 3—Add water until the soil is damp. Water this cup each day for the next two days. Place this container in a refrigerator or in an ice chest for the rest of the experiment.
   Cup 4—Add water until the soil is damp. Water this cup each day for the next two days. Place a piece of black felt over this container except when you are watering it.
   Cup 5—Add water until the soil is damp. Place several cotton balls that have been thoroughly covered with vaseline, so they completely cover the soil surface. Smear a layer of petroleum jelly around the top rim of the cup. Place a piece of plastic wrap on top of the petroleum jelly so that it completely covers the opening of the cup. Use a rubber band to firmly hold the seal in place (see Figure 1). This should keep out oxygen.

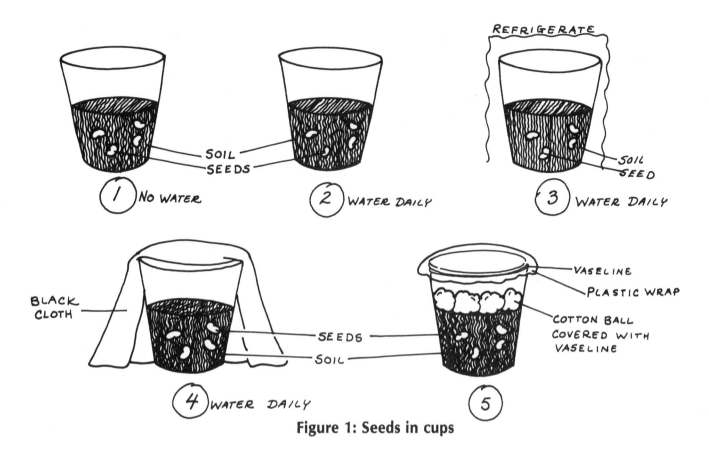

**Figure 1: Seeds in cups**

5. Place the cups in a location where they will not be disturbed for the next three days.

6. Each day for the next two or three days, observe what is occurring in each cup. Indicate in Data Table 1 the total number of seeds that have germinated in each cup.

**Data Table: Conditions for Germination**

|  | Cup 1 | Cup 2 | Cup 3 | Cup 4 | Cup 5 |
|---|---|---|---|---|---|
| **After 24 hours** |  |  |  |  |  |
| **After 48 hours** |  |  |  |  |  |
| **After 72 hours** |  |  |  |  |  |

## CONCLUSIONS:

1. In which cups did germination occur?

    _____

    _____

2. Is light required for germination? _____ Explain your reasoning.

    _____

3. Is oxygen required for germination? _____ Explain your reasoning.

    _____

4. Is water required for germination? _____ Explain your reasoning.

    _____

5. Can seeds germinate under cold conditions? _____ Explain your reasoning.

    _____

6. Define *germination*.

    _____

    _____

7. What is a *viable seed*?

    _____

    _____

8. List the conditions necessary for germination of a seed.

    _____

    _____

9. At what point in their lives do you think plants must receive light to survive?

    _____

    _____

# MAKING A DIFFERENCE . . .

**Objective:** Examine variations in heights among blades of grass in a grass population.

Evaluate ways in which variations among individuals within a population can affect the ability of those individuals to survive.

**Time Required:** Day 1—20 to 30 minutes
Day 10—50 minutes

**Notes to the Teacher:**
You may need to discuss with students Darwin's theory of natural selection. Define the terms, *mutation* and *DNA*. Explain to students that changes in DNA, called *mutations*, cause variations in organisms. Emphasize that these mutations are random.

Grass seeds are needed for this lab. They can be purchased from many retail stores, nurseries, or local garden centers. Johnson grass or packages of assorted grass work well. Plastic cups are also needed for this activity. Large cups with wide mouths are preferable.

Review metric measurements with students to reinforce what is meant by millimeters. Also review line graphing techniques if your class has trouble with this concept. Establish a location in a bright section of the room where the cups can remain undisturbed for 8 to 10 days.

You will see a great deal of variation in the heights of the grass. You should see that a few of the blades are very short, most are average height, and a few are very tall. These variations in heights will form a bell-shaped curve on the graph.

**Figure 1: Wide mouth cup containing soil and seeds**

# MAKING A DIFFERENCE . . .

A *population* is a group of the same kind of organisms living in an area. Individuals within a population vary to some degree. For example, the heights of students in a classroom vary. Organisms may vary in traits such as size, behavior, color, and skin texture.

The scientist, Charles Darwin, traveled around the world studying many different organisms in the nineteenth century. He noticed that no two individuals in a population are exactly alike. After observing different species of plants and animals, Darwin concluded that some variations in traits are inherited. Organisms with helpful variations survive and pass these variations on to future generations. Organisms with harmful variations usually do not survive. This process was named *natural selection*.

Darwin's theory of natural selection is sometimes referred to as "survival of the fittest." The steps of natural selection can be summarized as follows:

1. Living things usually produce more offspring than can survive.
2. Offspring compete for limited resources such as food, water, and shelter.
3. There are variations in the traits of the offspring.
4. Some of the offspring will have helpful traits.
5. The offspring with helpful traits will survive and reproduce.

Let's look at an example of natural selection. In a population of wading birds, some individuals have longer legs than others. These birds wade in the water to catch fish. They compete with one another for food. The birds with the longest legs can wade into deep water and catch fish. Birds with shorter legs are limited to shallow-water fishing. Therefore, the birds with longer legs have more food available to them and are more likely to survive and reproduce. As time passes, the percentage of birds with long legs increases in the population while the percentage of short-legged birds decreases.

**Figure 1: Long-legged wading bird**

In this activity you will observe some variations within a population. You will plant grass seeds and count the heights of the resulting blades of grass. Not all grass plants will produce blades of the same length.

# MAKING A DIFFERENCE . . .

**PURPOSE:** Determine variations in height among blades of grass in a grass population. Explain how variations among individuals in a population can affect the ability of those individuals to survive.

**MATERIALS NEEDED:**
Grass seeds
Plastic cups
Soil
Water
Metric ruler
Graph paper
Masking tape

**PROCEDURE:** **Day 1**

1. Plant 50 grass seeds in a plastic cup. Plant the seeds just below the surface of the soil.

2. Water the soil in the cup so that it is damp. Do not soak the soil.

3. Write your name on a piece of masking tape and place it on the outside of your plastic cup.

4. Place your cup near a window or other light source for 8 to 10 days.

5. Water your grass daily.

**Day 10**

6. After 10 days, use your ruler to measure the height of each individual blade of grass. You may have to pull out a blade after measuring it so that you do not duplicate the measurement.

7. Record the height of each blade of grass in the Data Table in millimeters. **Note:** All 50 seeds may not sprout, so you may have fewer than 50 blades to count.

## Data Table: Heights of Individual Blades of Grass

| Blade | Height | Blade | Height | Blade | Height | Blade | Height | Blade | Height |
|-------|--------|-------|--------|-------|--------|-------|--------|-------|--------|
| 1 | | 11 | | 21 | | 31 | | 41 | |
| 2 | | 12 | | 22 | | 32 | | 42 | |
| 3 | | 13 | | 23 | | 33 | | 43 | |
| 4 | | 14 | | 24 | | 34 | | 44 | |
| 5 | | 15 | | 25 | | 35 | | 45 | |
| 6 | | 16 | | 26 | | 36 | | 46 | |
| 7 | | 17 | | 27 | | 37 | | 47 | |
| 8 | | 18 | | 28 | | 38 | | 48 | |
| 9 | | 19 | | 29 | | 39 | | 49 | |
| 10 | | 20 | | 30 | | 40 | | 50 | |

## CONCLUSIONS:

1. Summarize the information in your Data Table:
   a. Find the height of the shortest blade of grass. Determine how many other blades of grass were the same height as the shortest blade.
   b. Find the height of the next shortest blade of grass. Determine how many other blades of grass were the same height.
   c. Continue totaling blades of grass in the same manner until you have accounted for every blade of grass.

2. Use the information above to make a line graph of heights of grass blades. On the "y" axis, place the heights in millimeters. On the "x" axis, place the number of grass blades of that height. Once you have plotted your points, connect them with a smooth line.

3. Looking at your graph, what can you say about variation of height among blades of grass in a population?

   _____

   _____

4. How could the height of a blade of grass affect its survival?

   _____

   _____

5. Do you think other groups of living things show variations? Give some examples.

   _____

   _____

# CHEF FOR A DAY

**Objective:** Determine the conditions necessary for yeast fermentation.

**Time Required:** Day 1—50 minutes
　　　　　　　　 Day 2—20 minutes

**Notes to the Teacher:**
Prior to the lab, discuss with students that yeast are microscopic organisms that can only survive under certain conditions. They perish when exposed to extreme heat, and in the absence of heat, yeast will not grow and multiply. Remind students that yeast require a food source to undergo fermentation.

Plastic drink bottles (12 or 16 oz.) are suggested for this activity. You may opt to use glass bottles or flasks. Students are also required to use hot plates to heat the yeast. If you do not want students using hot plates, you may omit Bottles 1 and 2 from the procedure.

Baker's yeast can be purchased at the grocery store. It comes in small square packages.

Caution students to do the following:
 a. To wear their safety glasses if using the hot plate and use pot holders or insulated gloves to handle the hot glassware.
 b. To immediately stretch the mouth of the balloon over the mouth of the bottles so that gas does not escape.
 c. To only use up to one-half package of yeast for each setup.

Discuss variables and controls. You can expect the balloon on Bottle 3 to expand. The balloon on Bottle 4 may expand slightly. The solution in Bottles 1 and 2 was boiled prior to the lab. This killed the yeast and prevented them from respiring. Bottles 3 and 5 were placed in warm environments, but only Bottle 3 had the yeast needed for fermentation. Bottle 4 had the required ingredients for fermentation, but it was placed in a cold environment. Bottles 5 and 6 both lacked yeast.

Humans must have oxygen to live. When humans inhale oxygen, it is used to help change glucose to energy in a process called *respiration*. Yeasts are organisms that can survive without oxygen. These organisms undergo a process called *anaerobic respiration*. This is simply respiration without oxygen. To respire in this manner, yeast must have a food that contains glucose. *Glucose* is a simple sugar that provides the starting point for this type of respiration.

During one form of anaerobic respiration, yeast produces energy and breaks glucose into a simpler carbon compound. This simpler compound then is converted to a form of alcohol, *ethanol*. During this process, called *fermentation,* carbon dioxide is released.

glucose ———> simple carbon compound ————> ethanol + energy + carbon dioxide

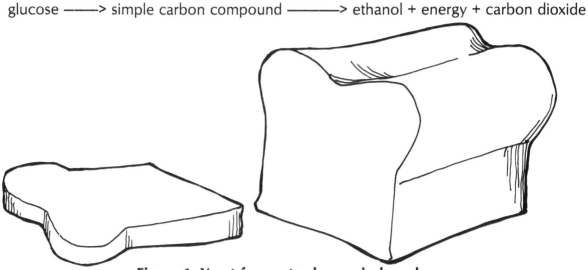

**Figure 1: Yeast ferments glucose in bread**

This may sound and look like a complicated process, but cooks use it in their kitchens daily. Yeast fermentation is used in bread making. Baker's yeast, when mixed with sugar, flour, shortening, and water, can ferment at about 25° C for an hour or more. During this process, yeast cells produce a little alcohol and a lot of carbon dioxide gas. As the carbon dioxide bubbles become trapped in the dough, they cause the dough to increase in size. The dough also takes on a lighter, finer texture.

The next stage of bread making is cooking. During the cooking process, the alcohol and carbon dioxide are driven off. The bread is light and porous due to the spaces created by the carbon dioxide bubbles.

# CHEF FOR A DAY

**PURPOSE:** Determine the conditions necessary for yeast fermentation.

**MATERIALS NEEDED:**

Dry yeast (Baker's yeast)
Six plastic drink bottles (12 or 16 oz.)
Six balloons
Water
Sugar
Teaspoon
Stirring rod

Refrigerator or ice chest
Hot plate
Two large beakers
Safety glasses
Hot pads or insulated gloves
Grease pencil

**PROCEDURE:**

1. Label the six plastic bottles 1, 2, 3, 4, 5, and 6. Put these aside for later use.

2. Place 500 ml of water in a large beaker. Heat the water on a hot plate until it reaches a slow boil.

3. Stir in one-half package of yeast and two teaspoons of sugar. Continue boiling the solution for five minutes.

4. Remove the beaker from the hot plate and allow it to cool. (While you wait for it to cool, begin step 5.) When cool, divide this solution equally between Bottles 1 and 2. As soon as you pour the solution into the bottles, stretch the mouth of a balloon over the top of each bottle.

5. Place 500 ml of water in a large beaker. Stir in one-half package of yeast and two teaspoons of sugar. Pour one half of this solution into Bottle 3 and the other half into Bottle 4. Stretch balloons across the tops of these two bottles.

6. Place 500 ml of water in a large beaker. Stir in two teaspoons of sugar. Pour one half of this solution into Bottle 5 and one half into Bottle 6. Stretch balloons across the tops of these two bottles.

7. Places Bottles 1, 3, and 5 in a warm environment for 24 hours. (see Figure 1).

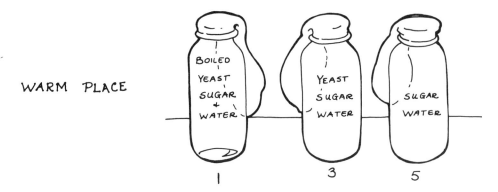

**Figure 1: Illustration of bottles in warm environment**

8. Place Bottles 2, 4, and 6 in a cold environment (ice chest or refrigerator) for 24 hours (see Figure 2).

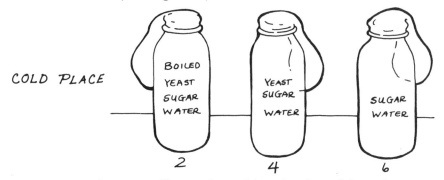

**Figure 2: Illustration of bottles in cold environment**

9. After 24 hours, observe what has happened to the balloon on each bottle.

10. Answer the questions in the Conclusions.

## CONCLUSIONS:

1. Which bottles have inflated balloons?

_____

_____

2. What gas do you think is contained in those balloons? _____ What produced the gas? _____

_____

3. Explain why some bottles do not have inflated balloons. Discuss each bottle individually.

_____

_____

_____

4. What ingredients are necessary for the fermentation process that is used in bread making? _____ What environmental condition is necessary for this fermentation? _____

_____

5. Name two products of fermentation. _____

_____

6. Explain how a baker makes yeast bread. _____

_____

_____

7. What happens to the gases and alcohol produced when bread is baked in the oven?

_____

_____

_____

# BACTERIA IN MY FOOD!

**Objectives:** Use bacteria in the preparation of a milk product.
Compare the rate of spoilage of homemade yogurt to plain milk.

**Time Required:** Day 1—50 to 70 minutes
Days 2 through 10—10 to 15 minutes

**Notes to the Teacher:**

Commercial yogurt is made by the addition of *Streptococcus thermophilus* and *Lactobacillus bulgaricus* to pasteurized milk. On a small scale, these bacteria can be transferred to cooked milk by adding small amounts of commercial yogurt with active cultures. The milk should be cooked to prevent the growth of unwanted bacteria.

People have been producing fermented milk products for centuries. Some fermented milk foods are *koumiss* of Central Asia and *leben* of Egypt. In all fermented foods, bacteria cause the milk to curdle and thicken.

A simpler, but more expensive, fermented milk product can be made by adding one-half teaspoon of yogurt to some heavy cream in a baby food jar. Cap the jar, shake, and incubate in a warm place overnight. The next day, a thickened, slightly acidic milk product is present.

To extend this experiment, have students produce their milk products under variable conditions. For example, after adding the commercial yogurt to their milk or cream, some students could place their beakers or jars in the refrigerator. Other students could heat their beakers or jars in a hot water bath. One or more beakers or jars should be maintained at room temperature as controls. Since bacteria are sensitive to temperature, those in the refrigerator will not grow, and the milk in refrigerated containers will not thicken. High temperatures kill bacteria, and yogurt will not be produced.

# BACTERIA IN MY FOOD!

What are the most common organisms in the world? You might be thinking about all the people on earth, or maybe the tremendous number of insects. However, there are more bacteria than any other type of living thing.

Because you cannot see bacteria, you may not know where they live. These microorganisms can be found in the soil, in the ocean, in fresh water, and on other living things. There are more bacteria living on and inside of you than there are people on the earth. Some types of bacteria can be found in places where nothing else can survive.

Most people are unaware of the bacteria around them. However, a few types of bacteria get our attention when they make us ill. Strep throat and Rocky Mountain spotted fever are just two of the illnesses caused by bacteria. Another time we notice bacteria is when they grow in our food. When large numbers of bacteria live in our food, we say that the food is spoiled and no longer fit to eat.

Like other living things, bacteria require certain conditions for growth. Most of them prefer an environment with a *neutral pH,* which is neither acidic nor basic. Some warmth is required for bacterial growth. That is why people refrigerate and freeze food to prevent bacterial growth. Bacteria must also have food, space, and water, just like other organisms.

On the other hand, many microorganisms are helpful, and you could not live without them. Some of the bacteria on your skin protect you from disease-causing bacteria. You have bacteria in your intestines that produce vitamins. Additionally, people have learned to use some bacteria to make food.

Fermented milk products have been made for hundreds of years. When milk is fermented, microorganisms in the milk change some of the milk sugar to an acid. This acid in the milk product prevents other bacteria from growing there. The acid also gives the milk product a distinctive flavor.

The action of these fermenting bacteria in milk cause milk to clump or *curdle.* The clumps are called *curds,* and the thin liquid around the clumps is *whey.* In the process of making cheese, curds are separated from whey by filtering. Some of the fermented milk products that you may know are buttermilk, yogurt, and cheese. The label "with active cultures" is placed on milk products that contain living, milk-fermenting bacteria.

# Bacteria in My Food!

**Purpose:** Use bacteria in the preparation of a milk product.
Compare the rate of spoilage of homemade yogurt to plain milk.

**Materials Needed:**

Dried powdered milk
Whole or skim milk
Commercial yogurt with active cultures
Hot plate
Small beakers
Thermometer
Stirring rod
Plastic wrap
Litmus paper
Tape
Marker

**Procedure:** **Day 1**

1. Pour 100 ml of milk into a beaker.

2. Add one-half teaspoon of powdered milk to the beaker of milk.

3. On a hot plate, heat the milk to boiling, stirring constantly.

4. Cool the milk to 45°C. With tape and a marker, label this beaker "yogurt."

5. Add one teaspoon of active yogurt culture to the beaker of yogurt. Cover the beaker with plastic wrap, and set it in a warm place overnight.

**Day 2**

6. Test the contents of the beaker with litmus paper. Record in your notebook whether the milk is acidic or basic. If the milk is acidic and thick, you have made yogurt.

7. Pour 100 ml of milk into another beaker. With tape and marker, label this beaker "milk."

8. Place the two beakers of yogurt and milk, uncovered, in a place where they will not be disturbed.

**Days 3–10**

9. Check these two beakers daily for the next several days. In the Data Table, record changes in the appearance and smell of the contents of these beakers.

| Days | Milk Appearance/Odor | Yogurt Appearance/Odor |
|---|---|---|
| 3 | | |
| 4 | | |
| 5 | | |
| 6 | | |
| 7 | | |
| 8 | | |
| 9 | | |
| 10 | | |

## CONCLUSIONS:

1. On Day 2, which is thicker—milk or your homemade yogurt? _____

2. Was the homemade yogurt acidic or basic? _____ Why? _____
   _____

3. On Day 1, why did you add one-half teaspoon of yogurt with active cultures to your cooked milk? _____
   _____
   _____

4. Why did you cool your cooked milk before adding the yogurt with active cultures?
   _____
   _____

5. Mold can grow on food and spoil it. After ten days, in which beaker did you have the most mold growth? Can you explain why you had more mold growth in one beaker than in the other?
   _____
   _____
   _____

# IT'S ALIVE! OR IS IT?

**Objective:** To determine the characteristics that distinguish living from nonliving things.

**Time Required:** One 50-minute class period

**Notes to the Teacher:**
Begin the activity by having students answer questions 1–3. While the class is answering these questions, prepare the demonstration you will do for them to answer question 4. Without allowing students to see the materials you are using for the demonstration, fill a petri dish about half full of water. Just as students are finishing their questions, add a small drop of Duco cement to the water. Place the petri dish on the overhead projector. The cement will react with the water. The pieces of cement appear to come alive and swim about wildly. Have students answer questions 4 and 5.

An alternative to using Duco cement is to use oleic acid which will coacervate in the dish. Students interpret this as living activity. A spine of a sea urchin dropped in vinegar moves as its calcium carbonate reacts with vinegar. You may also wish to place a living thing on the overhead, such as a petri dish of euglena.

The whole intent of this exercise is to get students to think. There are no wrong answers to any of these questions. Give students credit for using good thinking skills in answering these questions.

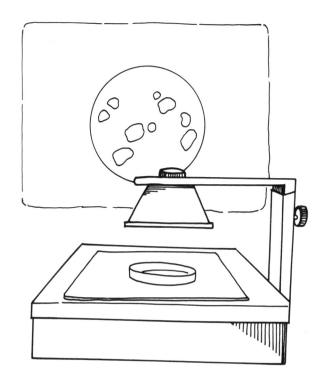

# IT'S ALIVE! OR IS IT?

The earth is a complex system of living and nonliving things. It is usually easy to distinguish between something that is alive and something that is not alive. However, there are cases when such distinctions are difficult.

All living things have several common characteristics. Living things are capable of movement at some time during their lives. You move from place to place, but have you ever seen a plant move? Plants do indeed move, especially in response to sunlight. Some plants even close their leaves and blossoms at night and open them again during the day.

Things that are alive must get the energy they need for life from their environment. Plants capture energy from the sun. Animals get this solar energy by eating plants or by eating animals that have consumed plants. Microorganisms live on and among plants and animals. Your body hosts millions of bacteria, quite a few protozoans, and some fungi.

Everything that is alive is made of cells or substances made by cells. The smallest living things are bacteria, which are simple, one-celled organisms. You are a good example of a multicellular organism, because you are made of billions of cells. Each cell in your body came from the cell that resulted from the fusion of an egg from your mother and a sperm from your father. The ability to reproduce is another important trait of living things.

Living things grow and develop. You do not look like you did when you were a fertilized egg. Immediately after fertilization, an egg begins to divide into many small cells. After several divisions, the mass of cells starts to change shape. One end of the cell mass eventually develops into a head, and the other end develops into hips and legs. Further development has made you into the young person you are today. Until you are about 20 years old, you will continue to grow and develop.

Living things adapt to their surroundings. Adaptations are traits that help organisms survive. For example, the white fur of polar bears keeps them warm and camouflages them in their wintry home. The wings of bats adapt them for hunting food in the air. The sharp teeth of wolves and tigers are adapted for tearing meat. And the flat teeth of deer and cattle are perfect for grinding tough plant herbs.

Nonliving things may show some of these characteristics. However, only living things show all of them. Can you always distinguish living from nonliving things?

# IT'S ALIVE! OR IS IT?

**PURPOSE:** To determine the characteristics that distinguish living and nonliving things.

**MATERIALS NEEDED:**

Pencil and paper

**PROCEDURE:**

1. Think about an organism that is alive. Write down three characteristics of this organism that identify it as a living thing.

    _____

    _____

    _____

2. Think about something that is not alive. Write down three reasons you classify this object as nonliving.

    _____

    _____

    _____

3. Classify the following things as living and nonliving. Explain why you classified each as you did.

    a. wind _____

    _____

    b. fire _____

    _____

    c. river _____

    _____

d. rose _____

_____

e. oak tree_____

_____

4. Watch the demonstration your teacher performs and decide whether or not the mystery substance is alive. List all the reasons you believe it is or is not alive.

_____

_____

_____

5. If an unmanned spacecraft travels to other planets to search for signs of life, what characteristics will the instruments in the spacecraft look for in the beings suspected of being alive?

_____

_____

_____

# ANY WAY YOU MEASURE IT

**Objective:** Measure two physical characteristics of matter.

**Time Required:** 50 minutes

**Notes to the Teacher:**
We are most familiar with the physical traits of matter. Matter's physical traits are those that can be observed and measured without causing changes to that matter. Mass, volume, and color are some physical characteristics. Students recognize a tennis ball because it has physical traits that are familiar to them. For example, the mass, volume, and color of all tennis balls fall within a known range.

Have students make a list of things that are considered to be matter. Some examples include people, clothes, desks, cars, food, and buildings. Then have them make a list of things that are not matter, such as time, ideas, opinions, motion, and energy.

Review with students use of the balance or scale. If they are not familiar with a graduated cylinder, show them how to read the volume at the meniscus. Ask them for examples of things that have a volume or mass that is generally measured. Their answers may include cereal, milk, roads, lumber, and clothing.

Before lab day, set aside several boxes, such as shoe boxes, that are easy to measure, but small enough to weigh on a balance.

Place several bottles in the room and ask students to read the labels and determine their volumes. Discuss metric units and English units. Discuss some common examples of metric units.

If you have a syringe, you can show students that one cubic centimeter equals one milliliter.

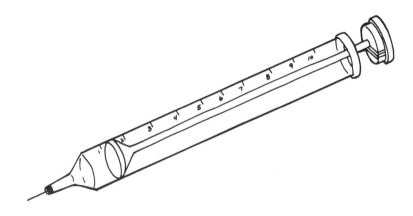

# ANY WAY YOU MEASURE IT

Look at the things around you. You are surrounded by *matter,* things that take up space and have mass. What are some examples of matter?

All matter has physical characteristics such as mass and volume. *Mass* refers to the amount of matter in an object. Mass is similar to weight, and you can determine mass by weighing.

*Volume* is a measure of how much space matter occupies. The volume of matter can be determined in several ways.

1. If the matter has measurable sides, measure its length, width, and height. Multiply all three of these numbers to get volume (see Figure 1).

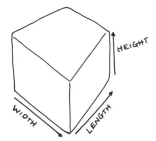

**Figure 1: Measure matter to determine its volume.**

2. If the matter is a liquid, pour it in a graduated cylinder and read the volume on the side of the cylinder (see Figure 2).

**Figure 2: Liquid in a graduated cylinder.**

3. If the matter is irregularly shaped, use the water displacement method. Add the matter to a known quantity of water and measure the amount of water it displaces (see Figure 3).

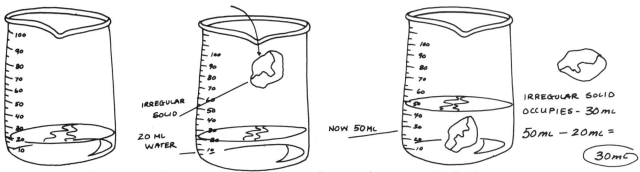

**Figure 3: The water displaced equals the volume of matter displacing water.**

# ANY WAY YOU MEASURE IT

**PURPOSE:** Measure two physical characteristics of matter.

**MATERIALS NEEDED:**
Balance
Metric ruler
Graduated cylinder
Shoe box
Marble
Paper cup of liquid
Assorted objects to measure

## PROCEDURE A: Determining Volume

1a. Determine the volume of a shoe box by measurement. Measure the length of the shoe box in centimeters. Then measure the width and height. Enter all three measurements below.

Length = _____ cm

Width = _____ cm

Height = _____ cm

1b. Multiply the length times the width times the height of the shoe box. Record your answer below.

Volume =_____ cm³

The volume is in cm³, one cm³ equals a milliliter.

2. Determine the volume of liquid in a paper cup by pouring the liquid into a graduated cylinder. Read the volume and record it in milliliters. Return the liquid sample to the paper cup.

Volume =_____ milliliters

3. Determine the volume of a marble by the water displacement method. Put some water in a graduated cylinder. Read the volume and record below. Add the marble. Read and record the volume again. Subtract the first reading from the second to get the volume of the marble.

Volume in graduated cylinder = _____ milliliters

Volume in graduated cylinder with water

and marble = _____ milliliters

Volume of marble = _____ milliliters

**Procedure B: Mass**

4. Weigh the shoe box on the balance. Record its weight below.

   Weight of shoe box = _____ grams

5. Weigh the marble, and record its weight below.

   Weight of marble = _____ grams

6. To determine the mass of the sample in the paper cup, pour the liquid into another container. Dry the cup thoroughly. Weigh the cup and record below.

   Weight of cup = _____ grams

   Return the liquid to the cup, weigh again, and record.

   Weight of cup and liquid = _____ grams

   Subtract the weight of the cup from the weight of the cup and liquid to find the weight of the liquid. Record your answer below.

   Weight of the liquid = _____ grams

**Procedure C: Volume and Mass of Three Objects**

7. Choose three of the objects your teacher has displayed for you.

8. Determine the weight, volume, and density of each object. Record in the table below.

| Name of Object | Weight | Volume | Density |
|---|---|---|---|
|  |  |  |  |
|  |  |  |  |
|  |  |  |  |

**CONCLUSIONS:**

1. Define *matter*, *volume*, and *mass*.

   _____
   _____
   _____

2. Describe three ways to determine the volume of matter.

   _____
   _____
   _____

# A DENSE SITUATION

**Objective:** Measure density.

Compare densities of water of various salinities.

**Time Required:** 50 minutes.

**Notes to the Teacher:**

Prepare "ocean" water using the recipe in the background information for students, and place it in a large flask. Place fresh water (tap water) in another flask. Label the flasks accordingly.

In this lab, students practice determining density. The formula for density is given in the background information, along with a sample calculation.

Students are also shown how to make the "ocean" water. Explain how the phrase "parts per thousand" expresses concentration.

Procedure steps 1–5 are fairly simple, and students can successfully complete them by following directions. However, Procedure steps 6–7 ask students to solve problems without giving them explicit directions.

a. Step 6 asks students to prepare a sample of water that is eight times saltier than the "ocean" water sample. It does not tell them how to prepare the sample. Since you used 3 grams of salt in 97 grams of water to prepare the "ocean" sample, students must put 24 grams of salt in 76 grams of water to prepare the "Great Lake" sample.

3 g of salt in 97 g water = 100 g solution 3 pph

24 g salt in 76 g water = 100 g solution 24 pph

b. Step 7 asks students to determine the density of their "Great Lake" sample. It does not tell them how to go about this. Students can deduce their procedure from the work they have already done with density.

# A DENSE SITUATION

The ocean contains several minerals, but the most common one is NaCl, or salt. The saltiness, or *salinity,* of ocean water is about 30 parts per thousand. To make a sample of water that has approximately the same salinity as the ocean, your teacher used the following recipe:

3 g salt + 97 g of water = 100 g of salt water

The salinity of this water is expressed as three parts per hundred. In other words, there are 3 parts of salt in a total volume of 100 parts of salt water. This is the same as 30 parts per thousand.

Salinity greatly affects which organisms can live in water. Some fish, insects, and plants require fresh water. Fresh water contains some dissolved minerals, such as NaCl, but in much smaller amounts than are found in the ocean. Ocean-dwelling plants and animals have special structures to deal with the water's saltiness. Some fish have pores through which they excrete excess salt.

The Great Salt Lake is saltier than the ocean. Depending on the weather, its salinity is six to eight times greater than the ocean's salinity. During times of heavy rain, the lake fills with water, diluting its salinity. Only a few organisms can live in such salty water. Brine shrimp and a certain type of fly are two inhabitants of this lake.

Since the ocean contains more salt than fresh water, it is denser than fresh water. Therefore, fresh water will float on top of ocean water. Density is a physical trait of matter. The density of matter can be determined by dividing the volume of that matter by its mass. The formula that expresses this calculation is

$D = m/v$ where D = density, v = volume, and m = mass.

For example, if the volume of a sample is 10 milliliters, and the mass of that is 5 grams, its density is

$D = m/v$

$D = 5g/10ml$

$D = 0.5g/ml$

# A DENSE SITUATION

**PURPOSE:** Measure density.

Compare the density of water samples of various salinities.

**MATERIALS NEEDED:**
Balance
Sample of fresh water
Sample of "ocean" water
One small paper cup
Graduated cylinder

**PROCEDURE:**

1. Weigh the small paper cup. Fill the small paper cup about one-half full from the flask marked fresh water. Weigh the cup and water again. By subtraction, determine the weight of the fresh water, and enter it in Data Table 1.

2. With a graduated cylinder, determine the volume of your sample of fresh water. Record this volume in Data Table 1. Return the fresh water to its container.

3. Completely dry the small paper cup. Add the sample of "ocean" water to the cup to the halfway mark. Weigh the cup and water. By subtraction, determine the weight of the "ocean" water and enter it in Data Table 1.

4. With a graduated cylinder, determine the volume of your sample of "ocean" water. Record this volume in Data Table 1. Return the "ocean" water to its container.

5. Using the information gathered in Procedure steps 1–4, determine the density of your freshwater sample and the density of your "ocean" water sample. Enter these densities in Data Table 1.

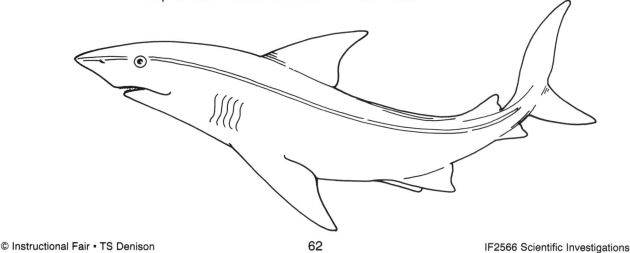

**Data Table 1: Weight, volume, and density of fresh water and "ocean" water samples**

|  | **Weight** | **Volume** | **Density** |
|---|---|---|---|
| Fresh water |  |  |  |
| "Ocean" water |  |  |  |

6  The Great Salt Lake is six to eight times as salty as the ocean. Make a 100 ml sample of water that is eight times as salty as the "ocean" water you used today. Refer to the recipe used by your teacher in the background information.

7. Find the density of this "Great Salt Lake" water. Refer to the background information and steps 1–5 of the Procedure. Record your information in Data Table 2.

**Data Table 2: Weight, volume, and density of "Great Salt Lake" water**

|  | **Weight** | **Volume** | **Density** |
|---|---|---|---|
| "Great Salt Lake" Water |  |  |  |

## CONCLUSIONS:

1. Compare the appearance of the fresh water sample to the "ocean" sample.

_____

_____

2. When a river enters the ocean, would you expect to find the fresh river water on top of the salty ocean water or vice versa? Why?

_____

_____

3. Why does the degree of salinity of the Great Salt Lake vary?

_____

_____

4. *Buoyancy* refers to how much water a floating object displaces. If you compared how you float in the Great Salt Lake, the ocean, and a freshwater lake, you would find that you float highest in the Great Salt Lake, next highest in the ocean, and deepest in the freshwater lake. That is, your body displaces the most water when it floats in the freshwater lake. Based on what you know about density, explain why this is so.

_____

_____

_____

# MAKING ATOMS AND MOLECULES CRYSTAL CLEAR

**Objective:** Examine a model of a salt crystal.
Devise a method of separating parts of a mixture based on the physical properties of those parts.

**Time Required:** 70 to 100 minutes

**Notes to the Teacher:**
Dried peas and beans can be used to make molecular models. Soak the peas or beans overnight before the lab. Connect the peas with toothpicks. As the peas and beans dry, they shrink and tighten around the toothpicks, making the models sturdy and easy to preserve. Introduce the symbols Na and Cl and the formula NaCl.

Sodium chloride crystals are cube-shaped. Each sodium atom is surrounded by six chlorine atoms. If time permits, students can also examine other salts such as hydrogen tartrate in cream of tartar, aluminum sulfate in some fertilizers, magnesium sulfate in Epsom salts, sodium benzoate (as an antimicrobial agent) in foods, and potassium aluminum sulfate in pickles and astringents. Also let students examine the labels of products found in the home to locate as many of these salts as possible.

Procedure steps 5 and 6 ask students to solve a problem. Do not give them any hints, but remind them that the background information provides clues that can help them solve this problem. Since all of the questions are open-ended, evaluate students' efforts and not their results.

| Criteria | Evaluation Rubric Points Possible | Points Earned |
|---|---|---|
| Model of salt crystal | 20 | _____ |
| Sketch of salt crystals | 10 | _____ |
| Sketch of sand crystals | 10 | _____ |
| Plan to separate salt and sand | 20 | _____ |
| Results | 10 | _____ |
| Plan to separate salt and water | 20 | _____ |
| Results | 10 | _____ |
| **Total** | 100 | _____ |

# MAKING ATOMS AND
# MOLECULES CRYSTAL CLEAR

Matter is made of small particles. If you could take one grain of salt and divide it in half, it would still be salt. Further divisions of this grain of salt would produce smaller pieces of salt. If such divisions were possible, you could continue to divide the salt until you reached the smallest piece of salt possible. This would be one molecule of salt.

A salt molecule is made of two parts: one part is the element sodium and the other part is the element chlorine. Therefore salt is a *compound,* a substance made of two different materials. The individual parts of a salt molecule are atoms.

*Atoms* are the smallest parts of elements. All atoms have a similar structure with a nucleus in the center. The *nucleus* contains positively charged particles called *protons* and neutral particles called *neutrons*. Orbiting around the nucleus are the negatively charged *electrons*.

The two atoms that make up a salt molecule are *bonded* together. The sodium atom has a positive (+) charge, and the chlorine atom has a negative (-) charge. Since like charges attract, the two atoms are held together.

The two parts of salt are very different from the compound salt. In the pure form, sodium is a highly reactive metal. It will burn explosively in a small amount of water. Chlorine is a gas that is poisonous. However, the compound made of one part sodium and one part chlorine is very stable and relatively harmless.

Solid salt is a crystal. The atoms of salt are arranged in an orderly structure, in a box shape (see Figure 1). The negative end of one salt molecule attracts the positive end of another salt molecule.

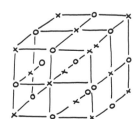

**Figure 1: Molecules of salt form a crystal**

When water is added to salt, the salt dissolves. That is why we say that salt is *soluble* in water. Water destroys the orderly structure of the salt crystals. Water is made of two hydrogen atoms and one oxygen atom. The oxygen end of a water molecule has a negative charge, and the hydrogen ends have positive charges (see Figure 2). Solubility in water is a physical characteristic of salt. Not all compounds are soluble in water.

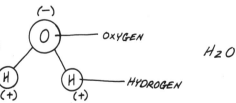

**Figure 2: Water molecule**

# MAKING ATOMS AND MOLECULES CRYSTAL CLEAR

**PURPOSE:** Create a model of a salt crystal.

Devise a method of separating parts of a mixture based on the physical properties of those parts.

**MATERIALS NEEDED:**

Two kinds of dried peas        Slide
Toothpicks                     Sand
Microscope                     Beaker or paper cup
Salt                           Water

**PROCEDURE:**

1. Using peas and toothpicks, make a model of a salt crystal.
   a. One type of pea represents chlorine atoms.
   b. The other type of pea represents sodium atoms.
   c. Toothpicks represent bonds between the atoms.
   d. Use Figure 1 as a guide for your model of a salt crystal.

2. Place a few salt crystals on a slide and look at them under the microscope.

3. Draw two or three salt crystals in the space below.

Salt crystals

4. Add a few sand crystals to the slide. Examine these under the microscope. Draw a few sand crystals in the space below.

Sand crystals

5. Salt and sand crystals look very much alike. However, they have different physical properties. Devise an easy way to separate the sand and salt crystals. Write your plan in the space below.

Plan to separate salt from sand particles:

6. Carry out your plan to see if it works. Record your results in the space below.

Results of experiment to separate sand from salt:

7. Mix 10 grams of salt in 90 grams water. Devise a plan for separating the salt from the water. Be able to prove that you recovered all 10 grams.

Plan to separate salt from water:

8. Carry out your plan to see if it works. Record your results in the space below.

Results of experiment to separate salt from water:

**Objective:** Determine how the addition of detergent affects the surface tension of water.

**Time Required:** 50 minutes

**Notes to the Teacher:**
Stress to students that the results of all groups may not be exactly the same. Remind students to drop the water in the middle of the wax paper and continue this process, one drop at a time, in the center of the wax paper.

Overall, you can expect students to accumulate many more drops of water than detergent water on the surface of the wax paper. The observations students make in Part A should cause them to predict these results for Part B.

In preparation for this lab, you may want to place a small amount of detergent for each group in a small paper cup to eliminate having to use one bottle of liquid detergent for the entire class.

As an extension, have students use common art materials to make a model of an insect that can be supported by the surface tension of water. You will need to give the class specific guidelines on the size of the insect. When the insects are constructed, hold a class competition in which students float their insects in a large tub of water to see whose insects float and whose sink. You may even want to award extra points for the student whose insect floats the longest. To make this activity more realistic, allow students to place wax on the bottom of the feet of their insects. This imitates the waxy substance that is found on the bottom of the feet of water insects.

WAX PAPER

DOME OF WATER
DUE TO WATER'S
SURFACE TENSION

ADDITIONAL DETERGENT
TO WATER GREATLY
REDUCES ITS SURFACE
TENSION

# LET'S MENTION SURFACE TENSION

The tendency of like molecules to cling to one another is known as *cohesion.* Water molecules stick to other water molecules. The attraction of water molecules for one another has an effect on the surface of a body of water. If you were to fill a cup to its rim with water, you would expect that the addition of more water would cause the cup to overflow. But if you add drops of water to the full cup, a dome of water builds over the surface of the cup. Continued addition of water eventually causes an overflow.

What causes the formation of this dome? A water molecule that is beneath the surface of water is attracted in all directions by the cohesion to other water molecules all around it. However, a molecule of water on the surface is only attracted by water molecules below and beside it. This downward pull on surface molecules causes the surface of the water to act like a tight skin. The formation of this skin is called *surface tension.*

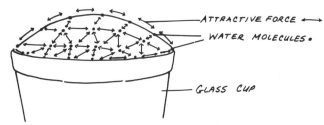

**Figure 1: Surface tension is due to the attractive forces between water molecules.**

Surface tension allows water molecules to cling together and form a dome above the surface of a cup. The dome continues to build until the pull of gravity overpowers the cohesive force of the water molecules. At this point water spills over the side of the cup.

Surface tension is not strong enough to support objects with a lot of mass. However, lightweight insects can walk on top of the water. The addition of soap or liquid detergent to water can destroy surface tension. As the molecules of detergent dissolve in water, they move between the water molecules, separating them. This breaks the surface tension, and the objects once held by the water will sink.

**Figure 2: Water insect walking on water**

# LET'S MENTION SURFACE TENSION

**PURPOSE:** Determine how the addition of detergent affects the surface tension of water.

**MATERIALS NEEDED:**
Wax paper
Medicine dropper
Dishwashing detergent
Metric ruler
Scissors
Water
Two paper cups
Paper towels
Tablespoon

**PROCEDURE:** **Part A**

1. With scissors, cut out a piece of wax paper about 20 cm long and 20 cm wide.

2. Fill one of the paper cups with water and place several drops of water in the center of the piece of wax paper.

3. Observe the appearance of the water on wax paper.

4. Use both hands to grasp opposite ends of the wax paper and carefully lift it. Tilt the paper gently from side to side and observe the behavior of the water.

5. Use a paper towel to wipe the water from the wax paper.

6. Stir about a tablespoon of detergent into a second cup of water.

7. Place several drops of the detergent water in the center of your dry piece of wax paper.

8. Repeat steps 3 and 4.

**Part B**

9. With scissors, cut two pieces of wax paper 15 cm long and 15 cm wide.

10. How many drops of water do you think you can place on this piece of wax paper?

11. Slowly place drops of water in the center of the wax paper. Count how many drops you can place on the paper before the water runs off the side of the paper. Record your results in the Data Table. Discard this piece of wax paper.

12. How many drops of water plus detergent do you think you can place on this piece of wax paper?

13. Slowly place drops of water from the cup containing detergent and water on a new piece of wax paper. Count the number of drops you can place on the wax paper before the water runs off the side of the paper. Record your results in the Data Table.

**Data Table: Drops of water on wax paper**

| Types of water | # of drops that will fit on wax paper |
|---|---|
| Water | |
| Detergent and water | |

## CONCLUSIONS:

1. Describe the appearance of the water on the wax paper.

   _____

   _____

2. Describe the movement of water as you tilted the paper from side to side.

   _____

   _____

3. Describe the appearance of the detergent water on wax paper.

_____

_____

4. Describe the movement of the detergent water as you tilted the paper from side to side.

_____

_____

5. Explain the difference in the surface tension of water and the surface tension of detergent and water.

_____

_____

_____

6. How many drops of water did you predict to fit on the wax paper? _____

7. How many drops of detergent water did you predict to fit on the wax paper? _____

8. Were you able to place more drops of water or detergent water on the wax paper? Give a reason for this. _____

_____

_____

9. Define *surface tension* in your own words. Explain how surface tension enables some small insects to walk on water.

_____

_____

_____

10. What effect does the addition of detergent have on surface tension?

_____

_____

11. Would insects that normally walk on water sink if detergent were added to their ponds? Explain your answer.

_____

_____

_____

# MONUMENT EATERS

**Objective:** Students will determine the conditions that may cause monuments to erode.

**Time Required:** Day 1 requires 20 to 30 minutes.
Five minutes each day for the next 10 days will be needed to collect data. Twenty minutes will be needed on the last day to answer the Conclusions questions.

**Notes to the Teacher:**

Remind students that monuments may be made of metals, limestone, or marble. All of these substances can be affected by acid rain. Acid rain is produced when rain drops from the air combine with oxides produced from the burning of fossil fuels. Review with students the concept that many metals react with acids to form new compounds.

If you do not have enough test tubes for this activity, you can use any small container. Be certain that the iron nails are not galvanized.

The test tube that contains iron wrapped with copper wire, salt, and vinegar demonstrates the environment most like the one surrounding the Statue of Liberty. Stress to students that the Statue of Liberty has been repaired, and the iron and copper are no longer in contact with each other today.

Your results should show that copper and iron in contact with each other will corrode more quickly than either metal alone. The presence of salt in any environment provides a conductor that increases the rate of corrosion. The presence of acid rain speeds up the reaction of metals.

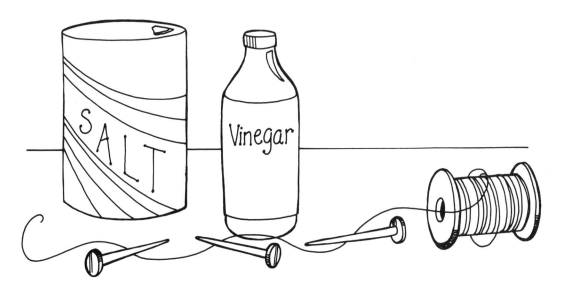

Monuments and statues located near the ocean often corrode. The Statue of Liberty is one such example. The famous statue, now over 100 years old, has a copper exterior. The inside of the statue is on an iron framework. A layer of tar was originally placed between the copper and iron to protect the internal framework from salt water. As time passed, the tar deteriorated and saltwater seeped inside this structure.

The copper exterior of the statue was chosen because copper is soft and easy to bend into various shapes. Iron was chosen as the internal frame because iron is strong and flexible.

Copper and iron, like many metals, can react with other substances to form compounds. The statue now has a greenish tint on the outside due to the reaction of copper with oxygen. The internal iron supports have reacted with oxygen to form a compound which you commonly know as rust. Chemical reactions sometimes occur more quickly when two metals are in contact with each other. Salt ($NaCl$) dissolved in water forms a solution that speeds up electric conduction between metals.

What role did acid rain play in this process of metal corrosion? No one knows for certain, but experts believe that the acid rain helped erode the statue. From 1981 to 1986, the Statue of Liberty received a massive remodeling job. During the remodeling, steps were taken to prevent further erosion. Special coatings were applied to the iron framework and a layer of Teflon was placed between the copper and iron. The cracks were sealed with silicone to keep out ocean spray.

In this activity, you will determine what factors have contributed to corrosion of the Statue of Liberty.

# MONUMENT EATERS

**PURPOSE:** Determine the conditions that may cause monuments to erode.

**MATERIALS NEEDED:**
Copper wire
Ten test tubes and stoppers
Salt
Teaspoon
Water
Six iron nails
Grease pencil
Vinegar
Scissors
Metric ruler
Sandpaper

**PROCEDURE:**

1. Label the test tubes 1, 2, and 3. Put these aside for later use.

2. Cut six pieces of copper wire into 15 cm lengths.

3. Use sandpaper to clean the outside surface of the copper wire and the outside surface of the iron nails.

4. Add the following items to the test tubes:
   Test tube 1—An iron nail that has been wrapped with a piece of copper wire. Sprinkle this with one-fourth teaspoon of salt.
   Test tube 2—An iron nail. Sprinkle this with one-fourth teaspoon of salt.
   Test tube 3—A piece of copper wire you wind up to fit inside the test tube. Sprinkle this with one-fourth teaspoon of salt.

   Pour enough vinegar in these three test tubes to completely cover their contents.

5. Test tubes 4, 5, and 6 should be prepared like test tubes 1, 2, and 3 except no salt should be added. Add vinegar to each test tube.

6. Test tubes 7, 8, and 9 should be prepared as 4, 5, and 6. Add water and vinegar to these test tubes. Salt is not added to these test tubes.

7. Place only a nail in test tube 10 to use as the control.

8. Place a stopper in each test tube and place the test tubes in a safe location. See Figure 1 for the experimental design.

9. Each day for the next ten days observe and record the changes in Data Table 1 that are occurring in each test tube.

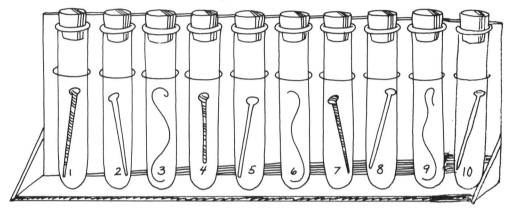

**Figure 1: Test tubes 1–9**

**Data Table 1: Observations of occurrences in test tubes**

| Days | #1 | #2 | #3 | #4 | #5 | #6 | #7 | #8 | #9 |
|------|----|----|----|----|----|----|----|----|----|
| 1 | | | | | | | | | |
| 2 | | | | | | | | | |
| 3 | | | | | | | | | |
| 4 | | | | | | | | | |
| 5 | | | | | | | | | |
| 6 | | | | | | | | | |
| 7 | | | | | | | | | |
| 8 | | | | | | | | | |
| 9 | | | | | | | | | |
| 10 | | | | | | | | | |

## CONCLUSIONS:

1. At the end of the experiment, in which test tubes were metals corroded?

   _____

   _____

2. In which test tube was the environment most like the environment of the Statue of Liberty?

   _____

   _____

3. If the Statue of Liberty had been located inland rather than on the coast, do you think it would have eroded as much? Support your answer.

   _____

   _____

   _____

   _____

4. In which situation would you expect to see the most corrosion: two metals that are in contact with each other, or two metals that are not in contact with each other? Support your answer.

   _____

   _____

   _____

   _____

5. If pollution had not caused acid rain, would the Statue of Liberty have ever corroded? Support your answer.

   _____

   _____

   _____

   _____

6. Explain the role of salt water in the deterioration of the Statue of Liberty.

   _____

   _____

   _____

   _____

# TOO HARD TO CLEAN

**Objective:** Determine some characteristics of hard water.
Soften a sample of hard water.

**Time Required:** 50 minutes

**Notes to the Teacher:**
Small, plastic, soft drink bottles work well in this lab. Have students bring some to school, or begin collecting them well in advance of the lab day. Baby food jars with lids also serve the purpose. If bottles or jars are not available, use flasks that are sealed with plastic wrap. Calgon is found at the grocery store in the bubble bath section.

To make hard water (sample A), add five teaspoons of Epsom salts to one liter of water. Heat to dissolve. Epsom salts can be found in grocery and drug stores. For sample B use soft water such as rain or distilled water.

Water that contains an excess of calcium, magnesium, or iron ions will not produce bubbles when mixed with soap and is called hard water. Water flowing over limestone, chalk, magnetite, gypsum, or dolomite often has high concentrations of these ions.

If hydrogen carbonate ions are also present in water, boiling will cause the formation of solid calcium carbonate on the insides of kettles, pots, and hot water heaters. Iron causes additional problems by staining fixtures.

Adding sodium carbonate, or washing powder, to hard water softens it. Hard water ions precipitate as magnesium carbonate or as calcium carbonate. These are washed away with the rinse water and the water is considered soft. Borax, trisodium phosphate, and sodium hexametaphosphate (Calgon) are other water softeners.

An ion-exchanger is a water softening device that can be installed as part of a home's plumbing. The ion-exchanger contains a resin made of zeolite, a material composed of oxygen, silicon, and aluminum. Zeolite resin is covered with many negative charges, which are balanced with sodium ions. As hard water flows through the ion-exchanger tank, calcium and magnesium ions are more strongly attracted to the resin than the sodium ions. Therefore, they replace the sodium ions and sodium enters the water. In other words, the hard water ions are exchanged for sodium ions. Sodium does not make water hard.

To extend the lab, have students devise other methods of softening water in the lab. Require them to design and perform one of their own water softening experiments. Another extension would be for students to test the hardness of water from various sources.

# Too Hard to Clean

Water travels through the world in the water cycle. Surface water in oceans, lakes, and streams evaporates. When liquid water evaporates, it changes to a gas. Water in the gaseous form is often referred to as *water vapor.* This vapor condenses, or changes from a gas to a liquid, on particles in the air. Droplets of water in the air form clouds. Sometimes the water in clouds falls to the earth as rain.

Rainwater is some of the purest water on earth. It does not contain any minerals, so we describe rainwater as *soft.* However, when rainwater strikes the ground, it can pick up minerals in the soil. Water that contains a lot of calcium, magnesium, and iron (three of the minerals that can dissolve in water) is called *hard.* Hard water can cause problems for homeowners. Therefore, it may be necessary to remove these minerals from water.

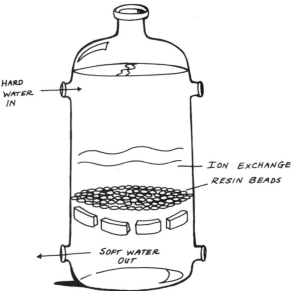

**Figure 1: The water cycle**

Hard water is undesirable for several reasons. Minerals in hard water combine with soap to produce a soap product that we call *scum.* Because the soap is tied up as particles of scum, it is not available to form suds. Soap scum can accumulate inside of washing machines and bath tubs and on clothes.

Water can be softened in several ways:
   a. When mixed with some detergents and soaps, the unwanted minerals will form small bits of solids. These can be washed away in the rinse water.
   b. Many homeowners prefer to soften their water with a device called a water softener. Water flows through this device, and the dissolved minerals are attracted to substances that remove them from the solution.
   c. Boiling softens water.

When hard water is boiled, dissolved calcium produces a rock-like scale inside of pots and pans, hot water heaters, pipes, and boilers. This scale, called *fur,* keeps much of the heat being applied from reaching the water. Therefore, more heat must be used to heat the same amount of water.

**Figure 2: A water softener**

# TOO HARD TO CLEAN

**PURPOSE:** Determine some characteristics of hard water.
Soften a sample of hard water.

**MATERIALS NEEDED:**
Water samples A and B
Calgon
Liquid detergent
Four bottles with caps
Beakers

**PROCEDURE:**

1. Label two of your bottles as A and B.

2. Pour 100 ml of water sample A into bottle A and 100 ml of water sample B into bottle B.

3. Place two drops of liquid detergent in each bottle.

4. Cap the bottles and shake vigorously. Examine the amount of suds or bubbles in each bottle. In the Data Table, rate the suds as: +++ for a lot of suds, ++ for moderate suds, + for few suds, and 0 for no suds.

5. After rating the water samples, put the bottles on the table and let them sit for about 15 minutes. Then examine each bottle for the presence of scum. (Scum makes water look cloudy.) In the Data Table, rate the amount of scum as:

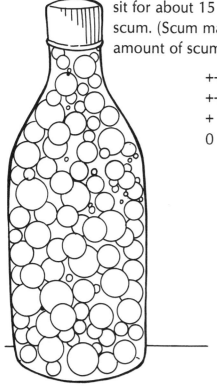

+++   for a lot of scum
++    for moderate scum
+     for little scum
0     for no scum

## Data Table: Amount of suds and scum in water samples A and B

| Water Samples Before Calgon | Amount of Suds | Amount of Scum |
|---|---|---|
| A | | |
| B | | |
| Water Samples After Calgon | Amount of Suds | Amount of Scum |
| A | | |
| B | | |

6. Label the other two bottles as A and B.

7. Place 100 ml of water sample A in beaker A and 100 ml of water sample B in beaker B.

8. Mix one-half teaspoon of Calgon with the water in each bottle. Calgon contains substances that chemically react with the calcium, magnesium, and iron in hard water to form a solid.

9. Repeat Procedure steps 2–4, and record your answers in the Data Table.

## CONCLUSIONS:

1. What is hard water?

_____

_____

2. What are some of the problems to homeowners that are caused by hard water?

_____

_____

3. How can hard water be softened?

_____

_____

4. In this experiment, which water sample was hard water? How do you know?

_____

_____

5. How does Calgon affect hard water? Explain your answer.

_____

_____

# LIKE DISSOLVES LIKE

**Objective:** Examine the properties of soap.
Make a bar of soap.

**Time Required:** 50 minutes

**Notes to the Teacher:**

Small, plastic, soft drink bottles work well in this lab. Have students bring some to school, or begin collecting them well in advance of the lab. Baby food jars with lids will also serve the purpose. If bottles or jars are not available, use flasks that are sealed with plastic wrap. In Part B laundry washing powder is the source of the base.

A soap is a sodium or potassium salt of a fatty acid. Solid soaps usually contain sodium salt and fatty acids, whereas liquid soaps more often contain potassium salt and fatty acids. Soaps have a nonpolar end, which dissolves in oils, and a polar end, which dissolves in water (see Figure 1). Because "like dissolves like," the nonpolar end of soap can dissolve grease and oil. The polar end interacts with water molecules (see Figure 2).

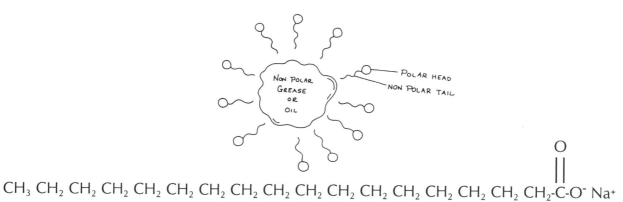

$$CH_3\ CH_2\ CH_2\ CH_2\ CH_2\ CH_2\ CH_2\ CH_2\ CH_2\ CH_2\ CH_2\ CH_2\ CH_2\ CH_2\ CH_2\ CH_2\ CH_2\text{-}\overset{\displaystyle O}{\overset{\displaystyle \|}{C}}\text{-}O^-\ Na^+$$

**Figure 1: A soap molecule**

**Figure 2: The interaction of soap, oil, and water**

Since ancient times, soaps have been made from animal fats and wood ash, a source of lye. In the nineteenth century, people made their own soaps from lye (sodium hydroxide) and fat.

Since soaps are salts of bases, they are slightly alkaline. Alkaline soaps can damage skin and some fabrics. Therefore, many soaps are pH balanced. Colors and fragrances are added to commercial soaps to make them more attractive to consumers.

# LIKE DISSOLVES LIKE

Water is called the universal solvent because it can dissolve so many things. A *solvent* is a substance that dissolves another substance, the *solute*. Even though water can dissolve a lot of things, it cannot dissolve everything. Water can only dissolve polar molecules like itself. Polar molecules are those that are negatively charged on one end and positively charged on the other end (see Figure 1).

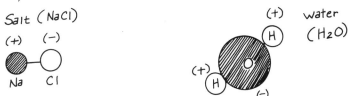

**Figure 1: Polar molecules**

If you were to take a bath in water, would you get clean? How would the dinner dishes look and feel if you washed them in water? Because oils are produced on your skin, washing with plain water does not get you clean. Likewise, the oils and grease from food need something more than water. Oils and grease are nonpolar compounds. That means that their molecules are not charged. Nonpolar compounds do not dissolve in water.

Since water is a polar molecule and oil is a nonpolar molecule, water cannot dissolve oil. Therefore, when you bathe in plain water, you cannot rinse the oil from your body with water. For hundreds of years, people have been using soaps. The most ancient soaps were made from water and wood ashes. Wood ashes contain a basic substance called *lye*. When lye is mixed with animal fat, it forms a soap.

Soap can remove oil and grease because of its unique properties. Soap is a long molecule that has a positive charge at one end, like a polar molecule. However, it has no charge at the other end, like a nonpolar molecule (see Figure 2). Therefore, soaps can interact with both water and oils.

**Figure 2: Soap molecules have a positive charge on one end.
On the other end, they do not have a charge.**

Soap molecules cluster around a droplet of oil, with their charged ends pointing away from the oil. Oil surrounded by a droplet of soap can be washed away.

# LIKE DISSOLVES LIKE

**PURPOSE:** Examine the properties of soap.
Make a bar of soap.

**MATERIALS NEEDED:**

Liquid detergent
Washing powder
Water
Oil
Baking soda
Small bottle with a cap
Graduated cylinder
300 ml beaker
Hot plate
Hot pads or insulated gloves
Small paper cups, muffin pan, or candy molds
Scales

**PROCEDURE:** Part A

1. Measure 50 ml of water and pour it in your bottle.

2. Add an equal volume of oil. (It is not necessary to measure the oil; estimation of an equal volume will serve this purpose.)

3. Place the cap on the bottle and shake vigorously.

4. Place the bottle on your desk. Examine the bottle immediately after shaking. Record the appearance of the oil and water in your Data Table.

Name _____

5. Continue to observe the bottle for five minutes. Record the appearance of the oil and water in the bottle after five minutes.

**Data Table: Appearance of oil and water before and after the addition of soap**

| Water and Oil | Appearance |
|---|---|
| Immediately after shaking | |
| After five minutes | |
| **Water, Oil, and Detergent** | **Appearance** |
| Immediately after shaking | |
| After five minutes | |

6. Add ten drops of liquid detergent to your bottle of oil and water.

7. Cap the bottle and shake it vigorously.

8. Place the bottle on your desk and observe. Describe the appearance of the oil and water in the Data Table.

9. Observe the bottle for five minutes. Again, describe the appearance of the oil and water in the Data Table.

**Part B**
10. To prepare a bar of soap, combine 50 ml of salad oil, 50 ml of water, and 20 grams of washing powder in a beaker.

11. Heat the mixture until it boils gently, stirring constantly. The mixture will become very thick. Continue to stir and heat for several minutes.

**CAUTION: HOT PLATES AND THE HOT CONTENTS
CAN CAUSE SERIOUS BURNS.**

12. Carefully set the beaker aside to cool. Before the mixture becomes firm, you can pour it into a small paper cup, a candy mold, or a muffin pan.

## CONCLUSIONS:

1. Define "polar compound" and "nonpolar compound." Give an example of each.

   _____

   _____

   _____

2. Is soap a polar compound or a nonpolar compound? Explain your answer.

   _____

   _____

3. Why did liquid detergent help your oil and water mix?

   _____

   _____

4. How does soap get you clean?

   _____

   _____

5. Another recipe for soap calls for vegetable oil, alcohol, and sodium hydroxide. Sodium hydroxide is a strong base. Which ingredient in your soap recipe do you think served as a base? Explain your answer.

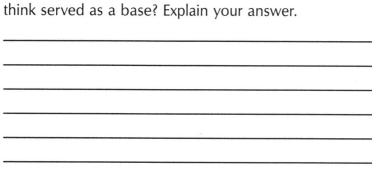

# POLYMER STRENGTH

**Objective:** Compare the strength of natural and synthetic fibers.

**Time Required:** 50 minutes

**Notes to the Teacher:**
If you do not want to use the fibers listed in Materials Needed, substitute those that are available to you. If you have some students who are willing to donate a few strands of long hair, it is interesting to test hair in this lab. If you would rather not deal with hair, silk thread can be substituted.

On the day before the lab, soak all of the fibers you plan to use in household bleach for 20 to 30 minutes. Bleach weakens these fibers. Without weakening them, students would be unable to measure the force needed to break the fibers with their spring scale.

Synthetic plastics are popular because they are inexpensive and lightweight. Ask students to suggest other materials that could be used to make something currently made of synthetic fibers, such as trash bags. Keep cost in mind during the discussion.

The fact that synthetic fibers will not degrade is causing a lot of controversy about their use. There are so many monomers in plastic polymers that bacteria cannot break the chains into smaller units. Some companies make "degradable" plastic that uses shorter plastic polymer chains that are connected by sections of starch. Since bacteria can break down starch, these plastics can be degraded into smaller pieces. However, many environmentalists argue that small pieces of plastic are no better than big pieces of plastic.

To extend this activity, consider having students research photodegradable plastics and plastics that contain corn starch. Have them compare the environmental impacts of these two types of plastics to nondegradable plastics.

Students can make some "milk plastic" in class. Milk contains casein, a protein. All proteins are polymers made of chains of amino acids. Compare the plastic students make to synthetic plastics.

### Milk Plastic

Heat a small amount of milk until it curdles. Pour off the whey (liquid portion) and keep the curds (solid portion). Add enough vinegar to form a blob of "plastic." Pour off any excess vinegar. Shape the "plastic" into a toy, then let it dry to harden.

# POLYMER STRENGTH

*Polymers* are very long, thin molecules that are made of repeating units. The individual units of polymers are called *monomers*. Most polymers contain 500 to 20,000 monomers (see Figure 1).

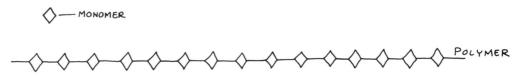

**Figure 1: A polymer is a chain of individual units called monomers.**

There are many natural polymers. Silk and hair are natural polymers that are known for their strength. The silk that makes up spider webs is stronger than strands of metal of equal size. Cellulose is a natural polymer made by plants that gives them strength and rigidity. Cotton is a strong fiber made of cellulose. Protein and starch are two other polymers found in nature.

Synthetic polymers are made by people. Small units of carbon atoms can be derived from petroleum. When these individual carbon units are chemically joined into long strands, they form synthetic polymers. These can be made into plastics or fibers. Plastics can be easily molded into desired shapes. Hard plastics are made by arranging the polymers in a very rigid structure. In soft plastics, polymers are free to move around one another (see Figure 2). Examples of hard plastic products are plastic pipes and cups. Soft plastics products include trash bags and the plastic that covers the telephone wire from the receiver to the base.

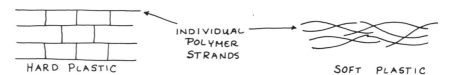

**Figure 2: Hard plastics have a rigid structure; individual polymers in soft plastics can move around one another.**

In synthetic fibers, strands of polymers have been straightened. These strands are arranged so that they lay side by side (see Figure 3). The individual polymers are loosely connected to one another, but they are also free to slide up and down. Because the polymer chains can slide, synthetic fibers are strong and flexible. Examples of synthetic fibers are nylon, polyester, and rayon.

**Figure 3: Fibers are made of long chains of polymers that lay side by side.**

# POLYMER STRENGTH

**PURPOSE:** Compare the strength of natural and synthetic fibers.

**MATERIALS NEEDED:**
Threads of polyester and cotton
A long hair
A spring scale
Ring stand with ring
Ruler

**PROCEDURE:**

1. Hang the spring balance from the ring attached to a ring stand.

2. Cut three 30 cm lengths of polyester thread. Tie loops in both ends of all three pieces.

3. Pick up a thread and place one loop over the bottom hook of the spring balance (see Figure 4). Slide a pencil through the other loop.

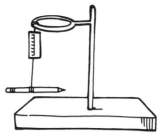

**Figure 4: Ring stand, spring balance, thread, and pencil**

4. Gently pull down on the pencil until the thread breaks. On the spring scale, read the force used to pull on the thread in newtons. (Force is measured in newtons.) Record your answer in the Data Table.

5. Repeat this test three times. Record the forces used each time in the Data Table.

6. Repeat Procedure steps 4 and 5 with the cotton thread and with the hair.

7. Average all three trials for each fiber. (For example, to find an average for polyester, add the three numbers that resulted from your three trials with polyester. Divide that total by 3. The resulting number is your average.)

Name _____

## Data Table: Force exerted on fibers

|  | Polyester thread | Cotton thread | Hair |
|---|---|---|---|
| Trial 1 |  |  |  |
| Trial 2 |  |  |  |
| Trial 3 |  |  |  |
| Average of all three trials |  |  |  |

**CONCLUSIONS:**

1. Define *monomer* and *polymer*. Give examples of natural polymers.

_____
_____
_____

2. How are synthetic polymers made? Name some synthetic polymers.

_____
_____

3. What is the difference in the structure of hard plastics and soft plastics?

_____
_____

4. In this lab, did you find natural fibers or synthetic fibers to be stronger? _____

5. Bleach weakens fibers. Why do you think your teacher soaked all the fibers in bleach before the lab?

_____
_____

6. Many synthetic fibers are nonbiodegradable. That means that they do not break down in nature into simpler substances. On the other hand, all natural fibers are biodegradable. What effect do you think materials made from synthetic fibers could have on the environment?

_____
_____

7. Take a survey of your classmates and decide how many are wearing clothes made of synthetic fibers (nylon, rayon, polyester) and how many are wearing clothes made of natural fibers (cotton, silk). Check the neck labels of shirts and blouses to get this information. Place checks in the correct columns. Some students may be wearing both; in those instances, place checks in both columns.

## Survey of Natural and Synthetic Fibers

| Student Name | Synthetic Fibers | Natural Fibers |
|---|---|---|
|  |  |  |
|  |  |  |
|  |  |  |
|  |  |  |
|  |  |  |
|  |  |  |
|  |  |  |
|  |  |  |
|  |  |  |
|  |  |  |
|  |  |  |
|  |  |  |
|  |  |  |
|  |  |  |
|  |  |  |
|  |  |  |
|  |  |  |
| Totals |  |  |

# GERONIMO!

**Objective:** Build a parachute that delivers your skydiver to the ground very slowly.

**Time Required:** Fifteen minutes on Day 1 to read background and discuss designs with partners.
One 50-minute class period to build parachutes and test them.

**Notes to the Teacher:**

This activity requires miniature toy soldiers or any other toy figure. You could also use toy animals or any other lightweight object. Clothespins would work if you do not have access to the miniature toys. Large garbage bags are needed for this activity as well as string and scissors. You will need to provide plenty of string so that students can experiment with various parachutes.

Prior to the activity you may want to discuss all the factors that can influence the fall time of a skydiver. Discuss the concepts of parachute shape, number of supports from the parachute to the skydiver, length of the supports, and size of the parachute. Tell students to begin thinking about how these factors can influence fall time.

Remind students that compressed air is a very powerful thing. Compressed air guns provide enough force to break concrete.

After students have measured and recorded fall time of their skydiver without a parachute, encourage them to give some careful thought to parachute design. This activity allows for a great deal of creativity on the part of students. Remind them that a good experiment only alters one variable at a time. If they choose to alter the length of support strings, they must keep all other factors the same. Without controlling these variables, it would be difficult to judge the effectiveness of the variable they are testing.

You may wish to encourage students by having a class competition on the next day and award a prize to the parachute with the slowest fall time. This activity needs to be carried out in a place where there is a large distance between the drop location and the landing zone. The top of gym bleachers and the top of stadium steps are good locations. Students must drop the skydiver straight down on each trial.

# GERONIMO!

You have probably seen skydivers parachute out of airplanes and land safely on the ground. How can skydivers feel certain that their parachutes will slow their descent toward earth? Perhaps they understand the concept of compressed air.

*Compressed air* is air that is squeezed together or compacted. You may not realize it, but compressed air is very strong. Compressed air machines are often used by workers to break concrete sidewalks. Compressed air in tires supports the weight of cars and trucks. And compressed air prevents a skydiver from falling too quickly toward the ground.

Any object that drops through the air carries *momentum.* Momentum is a force that is equal to the mass of an object multiplied by its velocity. The bigger the object, the greater its momentum. If you jump from an airplane thousands of feet in the air, you will strike the ground with a momentum that would kill you 99.99999% of the time. You can slow your momentum by applying an opposing force. Without the aid of a parachute, the ground is the only thing that slows and stops your momentum.

Skydivers certainly want to slow their momentum before they reach the ground. Parachutes provide this force to slow them by producing *drag.* Drag is the resistance to motion. Do all parachutes provide the same drag? In this activity you will attempt to discover the answer to this question.

As a parachute opens, air is trapped beneath it. Air beneath the parachute is compressed so it has a greater push than the air around it. This compressed air pushes upward and momentum is decreased. Gravity provides the downward force that is equal to the weight of the skydiver. The pushing of compressed air upward opposes this downward force. If the force of gravity is greater than the force of air pushing upward, the skydiver continues to fall. Even though the skydiver is not stopped, the compressed air slows him/her to a point where the momentum is not great enough to cause injury when contact with the ground is made.

# GERONIMO!

**PURPOSE:** Build a parachute that delivers your skydiver to the ground very slowly.

**MATERIALS NEEDED:**
Twine or string
Scissors
One plastic, miniature toy soldier or toy figure
Garbage bag
Metric ruler
Stopwatch

**PROCEDURE:**

**Part A**

1. Drop your plastic toy figure (your skydiver) from the top of the gym bleachers or any other high area. The figure must be able to fall straight down to the ground.

2. Your partner should be standing nearby with a stopwatch. Record the amount of time it takes for the toy to fall. Place this time in Column 1 beside Trial 1 in the Data Table.

3. Repeat this process two more times. Record your answers beside Trial 2 and 3 on the Data Table.

4. Average your three entries and record the average.

**Part B**

1. Using plastic trash bags and string, design three parachutes that you will attach to your skydiver to slow its fall. All three designs must be basically the same, varying in only one way. Either change the size of the parachute, the number of strings, length of strings, or the shape of the parachute.

For example, if you choose to test how size affects the fall rate of the parachute, all three of the parachutes you design must have the same number and length of strings. All three parachutes must be the same shape. The only thing you may change is parachute size.

2. Once you have designed your three parachutes, sketch and describe them in the boxes in the accompanying Design Chart. Indicate the size of each, the shape, the number of strings used, and the lengths of each string. Remember, only one of these factors can be different in each of the three parachutes.

3. Perform three tests or trials on the effectiveness of each of the parachutes. Use the stopwatch to determine the fall time for each parachute.

Find the average of all three trials.

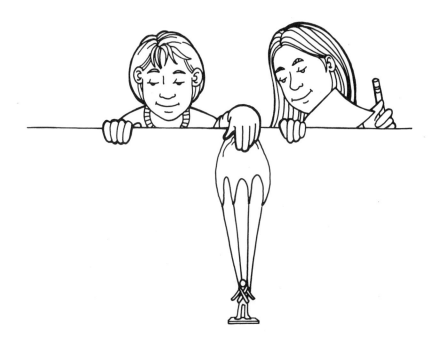

# DESIGN CHART

**Design 1—** _____
Number of strings used: __
Length of each string: ____
Length and width of the parachute: _____
Illustration of the design:

**Design 2—**
Number of strings used: __
Length of each string: ____
Length and width of the parachute: _____
Illustration of the design:

**Design 3—**
Number of strings used: __
Length of each string: ____
Length and width of the parachute: _____
Illustration of the design:

**Table 1: Fall time in seconds**

|  | Trial 1 | Trial 2 | Trial 3 | Average |
|---|---|---|---|---|
| **No parachute** |  |  |  |  |
| **Design 1** |  |  |  |  |
| **Design 2** |  |  |  |  |
| **Design 3** |  |  |  |  |

**CONCLUSIONS:**

1. Which design had the slowest fall time? Explain why you think this was so.

   _____

   _____

   _____

2. How does the size of a parachute affect fall time? If you did not test size as your variable, ask some of your classmates that tested size what they found.

   _____

   _____

3. Explain why drag is important to skydivers. Do you think that skaters and skiers want to increase or decrease their drag while racing? Explain your answer.

   _____

   _____

   _____

4. What is the relationship between compressed air and the amount of time it takes a parachute to fall?

   _____

   _____

5. Give some support to the statement that compressed air is a strong force.

   _____

   _____

6. What two forces must be equal for your skydiver to stop falling and remain floating in the air?

   _____

   _____

# PICK IT UP!

**Objective:** Determine how to reduce the effort needed to move a load with a lever.

**Time Required:** 50 minutes

**Notes to the Teacher:**

Rulers that have several holes or openings through them work best in this lab. These openings help students secure their weights to the ruler. Anything can serve as a weight. If you are using small bolts or washers, consolidate several of them in a small paper cup for each lab group. Students need at least 75 grams of weight to produce a measurable change on the spring scale.

There are three classes of levers: first class levers, second class levers, and third class levers. The wheel and axle and the pulley are also part of the lever family. A first class lever has its fulcrum between the load and the effort. The longer the effort arm, the less force needed to move the load. However, the longer the effort arm, the further a force must move to move the load. In first class levers, the load and effort move in opposite directions. See saws, scissors, and pliers are first class levers.

In a second class lever, the load is between the effort and the fulcrum. The effort and load move in the same direction. A wheelbarrow and the oars of a boat are second class levers.

In a third class lever, the effort is between the load arm and fulcrum. The load always moves further and faster than the effort. A fishing pole is an example of a third class lever. Your hand on the handle is the fulcrum. By applying a relatively small amount of force, you gain distance and speed.

To extend the activity, have students design second class levers. Place the weights on the six-inch mark and the fulcrum under the one-inch mark. Lift up with the spring scale. Compare the amount of force needed to move weight with a first class and a second class lever. Have students work with their second class levers until they have a design that uses as little force as possible to lift the weights. In a second class lever, the load is measured from the fulcrum to the load. The effort arm is from the fulcrum to the place where force is applied.

To demonstrate a third class lever, place the weights over the one-inch mark. Put your finger on the other end of the ruler to hold it down (do not press so hard that the ruler cannot be moved). Attach the spring scale on the end with the weights. Lift up on the spring scale. As you do, notice that the load and effort move in the same direction.

# PICK IT UP!

Any device that uses force to provide work is described as a *machine*. Machines make your work easier. Simple machines serve several functions. They can

    a. increase the amount of force applied to something,

    b. increase the distance and speed an object moves,

    c. transfer a force from one place to another, and

    d. change the direction of a force.

A *force* is a push or pull. When a force is applied to a machine, the machine acquires energy. This force might be applied with a muscle, by electricity, or the burning of gasoline. It is this energy that makes it possible for a machine to do work. *Work* is done when an object is moved through a distance. Work also involves a transfer of energy.

There are six simple machines, and they are the inclined plane, the screw, the wedge, the lever, the wheel and axle, and the pulley. No machine can increase the distance a load is moved and increase the force on the load at the same time. When the force on a machine is increased, the distance the load moves is decreased. Likewise, when the distance the load moves is increased, the force is decreased. For example, to move a heavy load up a ramp, you have two choices: you can use a short, steep ramp and push hard, or you can use a ramp with a more gradual slope and push less (see Figure 1).

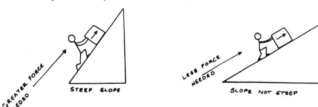

**Figure 1: A lot of force (push) is needed to move a heavy object up a short, steep ramp. However, less force can be used to push the same load up a ramp with a gentle incline.**

A *lever* is a bar that is put against a fixed point and used to move something or put pressure on something. For example, if you are working to remove the rocks from a yard, you might come upon a rock too heavy to lift. One way you could move the rock is by prying it up with a bar or rod. The bar or rod in this example is the lever. The point against which you rest that bar is the *fulcrum*. The force you exert against the bar is the *effort*. The distance from the fulcrum to the point where effort is applied is the *effort arm*. The distance from the fulcrum to the place where the load contacts the lever is the *resistance* or *load* arm (see Figure 2).

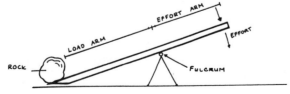

**Figure 2: Parts of a fulcrum**

# PICK IT UP!

**PURPOSE:** Determine how to reduce the effort needed to move a load with a lever.

**MATERIALS NEEDED:**
Ruler (one foot long)
String
Weights
Spring balance
Tape
Block of wood

**PROCEDURE:**

1. You will use the materials in this lab to design a lever that can move a large load with as little force as possible. The load in this case is made up of weights. The lever is your ruler. You will measure force with the spring balance.

2. Place the weights over the one-inch mark on the end of the ruler. Secure them with tape, if necessary. Center the block of wood under the six-inch mark. Position the apparatus so that you can connect the spring balance to the ruler and pull downward (see Figure 3).

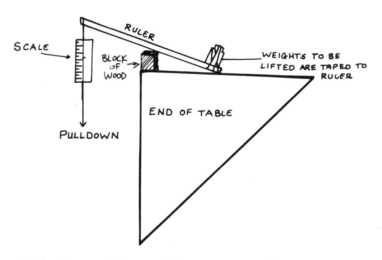

**Figure 1. The lever with a weight on one end and a spring balance on the other. The lever extends over the edge of the desk so that you can pull down on the spring balance.**

3. Pull down on your spring balance until the ruler is level. Record the amount of force applied (by reading the spring balance) in the Data Table under Trial as "Trial #1."

## Data Table: Forces applied to ruler

| Trial | Force Applied | Position of Load on Ruler | Position of Fulcrum |
|-------|---------------|---------------------------|---------------------|
| #1    |               | 1"                        | 6"                  |
|       |               |                           |                     |
|       |               |                           |                     |
|       |               |                           |                     |
|       |               |                           |                     |
|       |               |                           |                     |
|       |               |                           |                     |
|       |               |                           |                     |
|       |               |                           |                     |
|       |               |                           |                     |

4. Arrange the components of your lever so that you can lift the weights with as little force as possible. Each time you rearrange the load or the fulcrum, record their positions in the Data Table. Also record the amount of force applied during each trial. Repeat your trials until you are satisfied that you are lifting the weights with as little force as possible.

5. Sketch the lever that lifts with the least amount of force.

Lever that uses the least amount of force

**CONCLUSIONS:**

1. How do simple machines make work easier?

   _____

   _____

2. If you want to decrease the distance you must move a load with a simple machine, what should you do?

   _____

   _____

3. Explain how a see saw is a lever.

   _____

   _____

4. How did moving the fulcrum away from the weights affect the force required to move those weights?

   _____

   _____

5. Define:
   a. force _____

   _____

   b. machine _____

   _____

   c. fulcrum _____

   _____

   d. effort arm _____

   _____

   e. load arm _____

   _____

   f. load _____

   _____

# A VERY COOL ACTIVITY

**Objective:** Determine which materials make the best insulators.

**Time Required:** About 30 minutes on Day 1 for students to read the background, discuss the concept of insulation, and prepare the insulators they will use.
About 50 minutes on Day 2 to conduct the lab and answer the Conclusion questions.

**Notes to the Teacher:**

This activity requires four small plastic containers with lids for each lab group. You may want to collect margarine containers in advance of this activity or buy small, plastic containers at the grocery store. The larger containers can be a variety of things. The large food cans from the lunchroom are the right size. If you use these, remove one end of the can.

One day prior to the activity, allow students to read the background on insulation and discuss this information in class. At this time let students select the materials they will use as insulation. A variety of materials should be made available. A list of suggestions is given on the Background for Students page. Have students prepare their containers and write the names of materials they used in each container on the Data Table.

The night before the lab, fill some ice trays with water and place them in the freezer. You will need four cubes for each lab group. Make certain the water level is even so that the cubes will be equal in size. The next morning, transfer the ice cubes to a cooler or buy some ice cubes that are uniform in size.

The day of the lab, have students gather their materials and go outdoors. Caution students to quickly transfer one ice cube into each small plastic container to avoid excessive melting in the process. Remind students to check their containers every ten minutes, working quickly to determine how much water has melted.

Between the ten-minute intervals, you may want students to work on designing a container that would keep coffee hot in the winter months. Each group should turn in their suggestions at the end of class.

# A Very Cool Activity

You are probably familiar with the term *insulation*. People buy insulated jackets and have insulation installed in the walls of a house. *Insulation* is a substance that slows the movement of heat. Heat normally moves from an area of high heat concentration to an area of lower heat concentration. Sometimes the movement of heat is not desirable. Heat can leave a warm building in the winter, or it can melt ice cubes in your favorite soft drink glass. These are examples of undesirable heat movement.

Plastic foam, fiberglass, cellulose, and metal foil are some common insulators. Every insulator is assigned an *R-value*. An R-value is a measurement of a material's ability to stop heat flow. The higher an R-value, the greater its ability to slow movement of heat.

Think about your school building. When it was being built, insulation was placed in areas where heat was most likely to escape. This includes areas such as the ceiling, attic, and outside walls.

Insulation also prevents large amounts of heat from entering a building during the summertime. Therefore, the air conditioning system does not operate continuously, saving electrical energy.

Some insulators are better than others. For example, glass wool is a good insulator because it has air trapped between its fibers. Plastic foam is also a good insulator because it contains tiny bubbles that trap air. Air does not conduct heat. Heat loss can also be reduced by using shiny metal sheets and foils to reflect heat. Thermos bottles are glass bottles lined with silver metal. A partial vacuum inside the thermos reduces heat transfer.

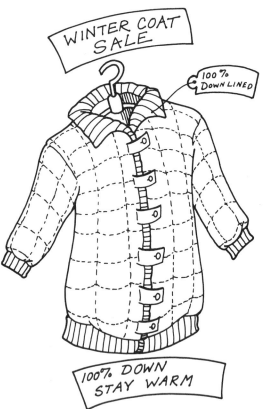

WINTER COAT SALE

100% DOWN LINED

100% DOWN STAY WARM

In this activity you will try to determine the best insulator to keep ice from melting on a sunny day. Remember that the best insulators are those materials that conduct the least amount of heat. This usually means the material that has the greatest number of air pockets is the best insulator.

# A VERY COOL ACTIVITY

**PURPOSE:** Determine which materials make the best insulators.

**MATERIALS NEEDED:**

Four small, empty plastic containers with snap-on lids
Ice cubes
Four large, metal food containers from the cafeteria
Various types of insulating materials: newspaper, sawdust, cotton
 cloth, polyester cloth, rayon cloth, packaging material, sawdust,
 socks, etc.
Graduated cylinder (50 ml or larger)
Colored marking pen
Ice chest

**PROCEDURE:**

1. Select three items to use as insulation.

2. Label your large metal food containers A, B, C, and D.

3. Label your plastic containers A, B, C, and D.

4. When you begin your experiment, place plastic container A in large,
   metal container A. Repeat with containers B, C, and D.

5. Use an insulating material to line the inside of metal container B. You will
   be inverting can B over plastic container B (see Figure 1). Leave enough
   space for your plastic container.

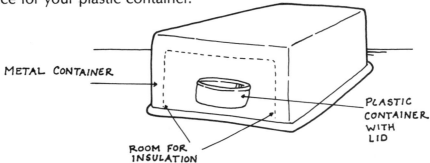

**Figure 1: Setup for experiment**

6. Use two different insulating materials to line the insides of metal containers C and D. Leave enough space for the matching plastic containers when the experiment begins.

7. Container A will have no insulation. Place the name of the insulating material you used in containers B, C, and D in Data Table 1.

8. Carry your containers outdoors into a sunny area.

9. Place the four plastic containers on the ground. Quickly place one ice cube in each plastic container and snap on its plastic lid. Quickly invert the matching metal cans over each plastic container.

10. Every 10 minutes for the next 40 minutes, quickly remove the metal cover of each container and look at the ice cube in each margarine container. Pour the water that has melted from the ice cube into a graduated cylinder. Record the amount you collect in the graduated cylinder during each 10-minute interval in Data Table 1.

**Table 1: Insulation and number of milliliters of water collected every 10 minutes**

| Letter | Insulation Used | 0 minutes | 10 minutes | 20 minutes | 30 minutes | 40 minutes | Total ml collected |
|--------|-----------------|-----------|------------|------------|------------|------------|--------------------|
| A | None | | | | | | |
| B | | | | | | | |
| C | | | | | | | |
| D | | | | | | | |

**CONCLUSIONS:**

1. Which material best insulated the ice and kept it from melting?

    _____

    _____

2. Which material was the poorest insulator for ice?

    _____

    _____

3. If you did not have a cooler for your cold drink at work, what could you wrap around your drink to keep it cool?

    _____

    _____

4. What makes a substance a good insulator?

    _____

    _____

5. Explain the rationale behind the design of a thermos bottle.

    _____

    _____

    _____

6. What is meant by R-value?

    _____

    _____

    _____

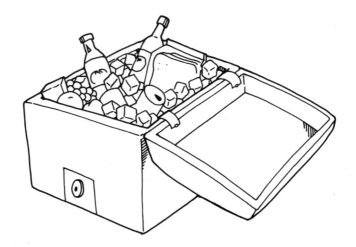

# How Far Is a "People Year"?

**Objective:** Compare a light year to a "people year."
Understand how light years are used by astronomers.

**Time Required:** One 50-minute class period

**Notes to the Teacher:**
This activity requires a large open area, preferably outdoors. A football field or playground would be a good location for this activity. Before going outdoors, you may want to discuss the following with your class:

1. the proper way to read metric units on a measuring instrument
2. the relationship between meters and kilometers and how to convert one to another
3. the relationship between kilometers and miles
4. proper use of the formula: Speed = Distance/Time
5. speed of light, 300 million km/second, maintains constant speed
6. relationships between seconds, minutes, hours, days, and years
7. proper use of decimals

The day of the activity, place students in groups of two or three. Each group should choose one person to run as fast as possible for ten seconds. This person will be called the *runner* for that group. His/Her speed will be the basis for each group's "people year."

At the beginning of the activity, have the class design a metric track. This 100-meter track will be measured in intervals of 5 meters. Each group will need a stopwatch to time ten seconds. You may want to check to see that each group knows the proper way to operate a stopwatch.

The calculation can be completed either indoors or outdoors. Each group may need a calculator.

This lab should show students that "people years" and light years can both measure distances. "People years" are not really possible because humans, unlike light, cannot maintain constant speed.

# HOW FAR IS A "PEOPLE YEAR"?

The Earth is just one small part of the vast universe around us. The closest planet to Earth is Mercury. We are about 58 million kilometers from Mercury. Pluto, the most distant planet from Earth is about 5.9 billion km away. Our sun, the closest star to Earth, is over 150 million km away. When we begin dealing in numbers that are in the billions or trillions, distances become very confusing. For this reason scientists have established a distance called the *light year*.

A light year is the distance that light can travel in one year or 9.46 trillion kilometers. If a star is eight light years from Earth, light leaving that star takes eight years to reach us. This means that things we now see happening on that star actually happened eight years ago.

Why was light chosen as the basis for calculating distances? Everything we are able to see is based on light. You see the words on this page because light reflects off the page and travels to your eyes. Light travels at 300,000,000 km/second so you are not even aware of the amount of time required for light to travel from the page to your eyes. On Earth, things are relatively close together, so you do not even notice any wait in time until you see things. For objects far away like distant stars it takes years for light to reach you. Even the light from the sun actually left the sun about eight minutes ago.

Excluding the sun, Sirius is the brightest star that can be seen from Earth. The light you see from Sirius actually left the star nine years ago. Sirius is nine light years from Earth.

Light can be thought of as a messenger that carries information from one point to another. The time it takes to deliver the message depends on the speed of the messenger. What if a person was the messenger instead of light? Could you measure distances in terms of "people years"? To do so, you must remember that your messenger person never speeds up or slows down. He/She must maintain a constant speed, just as light maintains a constant speed. Let's try measuring distance with "people years."

# HOW FAR IS A "PEOPLE YEAR"?

**PURPOSE:** Compare a light year to a "people year."
Understand how light years are used by astronomers.

**MATERIALS NEEDED:**
Metric tape
Large outside area
Stopwatch
Calculators
String
Paper and markers
Masking tape

**PROCEDURE:**
1. In the parking lot or other open area, design a metric track for the entire class by completing the following:
   a. Tape a piece of paper labeled *Start* on the ground.
   b. Use the metric ruler to measure five meters from Start. Mark this spot by taping a paper labeled *five meters* at this location on the ground.
   c. Measure five more meters from the five-meter spot and mark this location as *ten meters.*
   d. Continue this process in intervals of five meters until you have reached 100 meters.

   The class will use this track to conduct the experiment.

2. Each group should select one person to be the runner. The runner will run as fast and as far as he/she can in ten seconds. The other members of that group will operate the stopwatch and mark the runner's location at the end of the allotted time.

3. If the runner lands between the five-meter marks, you may measure the exact location using the metric ruler. Record the distance your runner covered in ten seconds in your notebook.

**Calculations:**

1. Determine the speed your runner traveled by using the formula: Speed = Distance/Time. Your answer will be in meters/second.

2. Convert the speed of your runner to km/second by dividing your answer to Calculation #1 by 1,000.

3. Convert your speed from Calculation #2 in km/sec to km/minute by multiplying by 60.

4. Convert the speed in km/minute from Calculation #3 to km/hour by multiplying again by 60.

5. Convert the speed in km/hour from Calculation #4 to km/day by multiplying by 24.

6. Convert the speed in km/day from Calculation #5 to km/year by multiplying by 365.

7. Your answer from Calculation #6 is the number of km your runner could travel in one year. We will call this a "people year." If your runner could run nonstop for one year, this is the distance in km he/she could cover. Explain how you could determine how many "people years" you are from Sirius, the nearest star.

8. Explain how you would determine the number of "people years" you are from the sun.

## CONCLUSIONS:

1. Define a "people year."

_____

_____

2. If a star is 25 light years away from earth, what does this mean?

_____

_____

3. Why is light, instead of people, used in calculating distances?

_____

_____

4. How are "people years" and light years similar? How are they different?

_____

_____

# DISTANCES AND DIAMETERS

**Objective:** Determine the diameter of unknown objects using angular diameter.
Determine the diameter of the moon.

**Time Required:** One 50-minute period on Day 1.
About 25 to 30 minutes for homework that night.
About 20 to 30 minutes on Day 2.

**Notes to the Teacher:**

A good way to begin this activity is to ask students if they think the moon is bigger than the stars. Most students will know that the stars look smaller than the moon because they are farther away. From this you can tell students that distance is important in determining diameter of objects.

Show them how to use the formula discussed in Background for Students. Demonstrate using a coin to block the view of a round object by moving the coin close to and away from your eye. Have them try this so they can see how distance makes a big difference.

Solving the equation in this activity requires some math skill. Reinforce the art of cross multiplying and solving for an unknown. An example problem is given in the Procedure.

You will need three balls of different sizes for this activity. A large ball, medium ball, and small ball might be a basketball, volleyball, and softball. Tell students that these are three planets whose diameters are unknown. Their responsibility is to find the diameter without actually measuring the balls with a ruler. You should measure the diameters of the balls before class. Students will need this information on Day 2.

A homework assignment is given to determine the diameter of the moon. You may have to omit this part if you do not have a full moon or a clear night when the outline of a full moon can be seen.

# DISTANCES AND DIAMETERS

Can you determine the diameter of the moon, the sun, and many of the planets? Obviously you cannot travel to these places with a meter stick and measure them. But there is a simple technique you can use to discover fairly accurate diameters of faraway objects without ever leaving earth. This technique involves ratios and proportions.

The ratio and proportion technique can be used by measuring the *angular diameter*. The angular diameter of an object such as the moon can be found by choosing your location on the earth and drawing a straight line to the bottom of the moon and then drawing another straight line to the top of the moon. The angle formed between these lines is ½ degree. This is the angular diameter of the moon (see Figure 1).

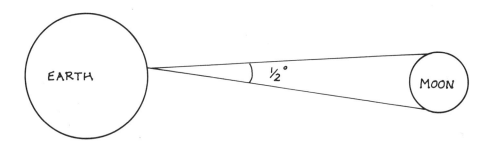

**Figure 1: Angular diameter of the moon**

Even though two objects are not the same size, they can have the same angular diameter. Take the moon for instance. Hold up a coin between one eye and the full moon. Close one eye and move the coin further or closer to your open eye until the coin completely blocks the moon from view. At this point, the coin and the moon have the same angular diameter. When two objects have the same angular diameter, they appear to be the same size. The apparent size of an object depends on how close or far away it is from your view.

Angular diameters are only useful if you know the distance to the object you are measuring. If you know the distance from the coin to your eye when it blocks the view of the moon, the diameter of the coin, and the distance from the earth to the moon, you can find the diameter of the moon. The following formula is used to do this.

$$\frac{\underline{\text{Coin diameter}}}{\text{Coin distance to eye}} = \frac{\underline{\text{Diameter of object being measured}}}{\text{Distance to object being measured}}$$

# DISTANCES AND DIAMETERS

**PURPOSE:** Determine the diameter of unknown objects using angular diameter.
Determine the diameter of the moon.

**MATERIALS NEEDED:**
Balls of three different sizes (large, medium, and small), such as a basketball, tennis ball, golf ball, volleyball, softball, etc.
A shelf or other piece of furniture that is about as tall as your students (or students can sit down for this activity and use desks)
A quarter, dime, and penny
Metric ruler

**PROCEDURE:** **Part A**

1. Place the largest ball on a shelf or on a piece of furniture so that it is about eye level. The ball represents a large object in the universe. Using angular diameter, you can determine the diameter of the ball without actually measuring it. (At no time in the activity should you use the ruler to measure the ball's diameter. Your teacher will provide you with answers later in the activity so that you can check your accuracy.)

2. Close one eye and hold the quarter at arm's length between your open eye and the ball. Move the quarter back and forth until you establish a place where the quarter completely blocks the view of the large ball. If this is not possible, step back a few more steps and try this procedure again.

3. Once you have blocked your view of the ball, have your partner measure the distance between your eye and the coin in centimeters. Record this in Data Table 1 beside "Large Ball." Measure the distance between where you are standing and the ball and record in centimeters in Data Table 1. Finally, measure the diameter of the quarter and record in Data Table 1.

4. Change roles with your partner and repeat this process. Partner B should record his/her findings in Data Table 2.

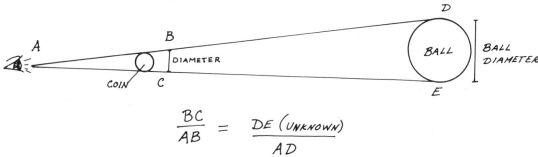

$$\frac{BC}{AB} = \frac{DE\ (\text{UNKNOWN})}{AD}$$

Name _____

**Data Table 1—Partner A—(Name: _____)**

|  | Diameter of coin | Distance of coin from your eye | Distance from you to the ball | Diameter of the ball |
|---|---|---|---|---|
| Large Ball |  |  |  | Unknown |
| Medium Ball |  |  |  | Unknown |
| Small Ball |  |  |  | Unknown |

**Data Table 2—Partner B—(Name: _____)**

|  | Diameter of coin | Distance of coin from your eye | Distance from you to the ball | Diameter of the ball |
|---|---|---|---|---|
| Large Ball |  |  |  | Unknown |
| Medium Ball |  |  |  | Unknown |
| Small Ball |  |  |  | Unknown |

5. Repeat the above process using the medium ball and a penny. Both partners should record their results in their data tables.

6. Repeat the process using the small ball and a dime. Both partners should record their results in their data tables.

7. Figure 2 shows how you can use the coin's diameter to determine the unknown diameter of an object. Notice that the diameter of the coin compared to the distance between your eye and the coin is equal to the diameter of the ball compared to the distance between you and the ball.

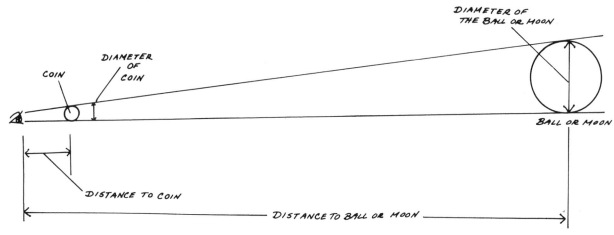

**Figure 2: Use ratio and proportion of angular diameter to determine the unknown diameter of an object.**

8. Use the equation that follows to find the diameter of the three balls. Record your answer in Data Table 3.

$$\frac{\text{Diameter of coin used}}{\text{Distance from your eye to coin}} = \frac{\text{Diameter of ball (the unknown)}}{\text{Distance from you to ball}}$$

Before finding the diameter of the balls, study the following example of finding the diameter of a paper plate. Once you understand the example, use the above equation to find the diameter of the three balls in this activity. Record your answers in centimeters in the charts on the next page.

**Example problem:**
You use a nickel to block the view of a paper plate. The diameter of the nickel is 2.5 cm. The diameter of the plate is the unknown. You hold the nickel 22 centimeters from your open eye and step back 270 centimeters from the plate. Your calculations look like this:

$$\frac{2.5 \text{cm}}{22 \text{ cm}} = \frac{\text{Unknown}}{270 \text{ cm}}$$

**To solve this:** Cross multiply 2.5 cm x 270 cm. This equals 675 cm.
Cross multiply the 22 cm x the unknown and you get 22 cm unknown.
To solve the unknown, divide 675 cm by 22 cm. Your answer is 30.6 cm. This is the diameter of the plate.

### Data Table 3: Results of Activity

|  | Partner A | Partner B |
|---|---|---|
| Diameter of Large Ball |  |  |
| Diameter of Medium Ball |  |  |
| Diameter of Small Ball |  |  |

**Part B: Diameter of the moon**

1. Using the same procedure, at home tonight calculate the diameter of the moon. You may use any coin you have available.

2. The moon, rather than the ball, is the unknown.

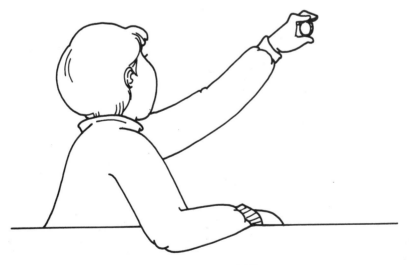

3. The distance from the earth to the moon is 38,440,100,000 centimeters. You will use large numbers to solve this equation, so be careful.

4. Below, show how you set up the equation. Circle your answer.

## CONCLUSIONS:

1. Your teacher will give you the true diameter of the balls. Compare these to the diameters you found with your equations. How do they compare? What could account for any differences?

   _____

   _____

2. Your teacher will give you the true diameter of the moon. Compare this to the diameter you calculated. How do they compare? What could account for any differences?

   _____

   _____

3. Were the different coins equally effective in calculating diameters? Explain your answer.

   _____

   _____

4. If you saw a round object in the sky that was reported to be a weather balloon, explain how you could determine the size of that balloon. The weather station has information available on how close the balloon is to different cities. What equipment would you use? Draw an illustration that helps explain the procedure you used.

   _____

   _____

# DINOSAUR FEET

**Objective:** Analyze footprints to find clues to animal behavior.

**Time Required:** 50 minutes

**Notes to the Teacher:**
It is difficult for all of us to relate to the amount of time that has passed since earth's formation. Such long periods of time are referred to by geologists as "deep time." Compared to the rest of our universe, the earth is fairly young. Scientists estimate that the universe is at least three times as old as the earth.

The dinosaurs lived in one of the most interesting segments of earth's history. Never before have such enormous animals dominated the earth. We tend to think that the dinosaurs lived a long time ago. However, 95% of the earth's history had passed by the time the dinosaurs made their appearance.

You might want to have students develop a time line to keep earth's history in perspective. Establish a scale so that one centimeter, or one meter, represents 100 million years. Keep in mind that using the centimeter scale, the entire Cenozoic era is squeezed into a little more than 5 millimeters.

The eras of times since earth's formation:

| | |
|---|---|
| Precambrian | 4,600 to 570 million years ago<br>Bacteria and some algae developed |
| Cambrian | 570 to 245 million years ago<br>Most major groups of plants and animals appeared<br>Plants and animals moved from water to land |
| Mesozoic | 245 to 65 million years ago<br>Dinosaurs dominated the earth |
| Cenozoic | 65 million years ago to present<br>Mammals developed; humanoids appeared |

# DINOSAUR FEET

Earth, and the things that live on it, have changed over time. Scientists who study fossils of plants and animals are beginning to piece together some information about early life on earth. A *fossil* is an imprint or a part of an organism that lived a long time ago.

The earth is 4.6 billion years old. By 570 million years ago, most land plants and animals had developed. Dinosaurs, one of history's most interesting groups, appeared 230 million years ago. Humans are newcomers on earth. The earliest human fossils date back to 7 million years.

By looking at fossils, scientists can determine how early animals probably looked. However, it is very difficult to know how these animals behaved. *Trackways* are fossilized animal tracks that reveal some clues to early animal behavior. Trackways are usually found in sedimentary rock. Rock formed by compressing layers of solid is called *sedimentary* rock. After animals traveled through damp soil and left their tracks, soil accumulated on top of the tracks. Other layers of soil were added on top of the dirt in these tracks. Over time, the pressure of many layers left permanent prints in the soil.

A lot can be learned from tracks. Heavy animals leave the deepest tracks. Lightweight animals do not sink as deeply in the soil. The footprints of animals who are running are spread further apart than footprints of those same animals who are walking.

Scientists would like to know whether dinosaurs lived and traveled in cooperative groups, or whether each individual dinosaur lived alone. Trackways help them understand this kind of behavior. Animals who live in groups usually travel in an organized manner. Some groups have one leader whom everyone else follows. For example, geese fly in a V-shaped pattern, with the leader in the middle. Other groups have a leader, but differ from geese by keeping their young and weak guarded between strong adults. Elephants are led by a female. Behind her, other members of the group shepherd the babies among them.

On the other hand, some dinosaurs obviously travel and hunt alone. One set of tracks, without any similar tracks deposited in the same time period, suggests loners.

# DINOSAUR FEET

**PURPOSE:** Analyze footprints to find clues to animal behavior.

**MATERIALS NEEDED:** Footprint handout
Colored pencils

**PROCEDURE:**
1. Examine the Footprint Handout. Notice that there are a lot of tracks on the handout. Each animal's tracks are labeled with a number so that you can follow the movements of that animal through the area.

   The footprints of two kinds of animals are presented here:
   a. Long-necked plant-eating dinosaurs that walked on all fours (see Figure 1)

   b. Meat eaters who stood upright on muscular feet and legs (see Figure 2)

2. Examine the footprints. Color each individual's tracks a different color. Then answer the Conclusion questions.

**CONCLUSIONS:**

1. What is a fossil?

   _____

   _____

2. How do parts of living things become fossilized?

   _____

   _____

3. Igneous rock is produced by extreme heat. Why don't we find any fossils in igneous rock?

_____

_____

4. Which animal was the first one to travel through the area? How can you tell?

_____

_____

5. Who entered the area first, animal #8 or animal #6? How do you know?

_____

_____

6. Were the plant eaters traveling as a group? Were the meat eaters traveling as a group? How do you know?

_____

_____

_____

_____

7. When did animal #2 travel through the area? How do you know?

_____

_____

_____

_____

8. What do you think animal #9 might have been doing? Explain your reasoning.

_____

_____

9. Which animal was probably older, animal #5 or animal #7? How can you tell?

_____

_____

10. Do you think there was a fight in this area? Why or why not?

_____

_____

# IT'S A DIRTY JOB BUT SOMEBODY HAS TO DO IT!

**Objective:** Compare the drainage of water through different soil types.

**Time Required:** One 50-minute class period

**Notes to the Teacher:**

This activity requires three different types of soil: sand, clay, and loam. Sand can be purchased at your local masonry establishments if it is not available in your area. If clay soil is not available in your area, you can use potter's clay. Loam can be purchased from nurseries and local stores as potting soil.

Caution students to be careful using scissors while preparing their bottles as filtering devices. Throw away the caps that come on the bottles.

Before beginning this activity, ask students to feel the texture of the three types of soil. Discuss how each soil feels. Have students dampen a small amount of each soil and roll it in their hands. Clay soil sticks together and can be rolled into a tube shape. Loam does not stick together well. Sand does not stick at all. Ask students how the ability to stick together may influence a soil's water-holding ability. You could further extend this activity by allowing students to use dissecting microscopes to examine the soil particles found in each soil type.

Discuss the difference in organic and inorganic matter in soil. Remind students that soil that is pure sand, silt, or clay is inorganic. Loam contains decayed matter, so it contains organic components. Students may ask what type soil is on the playground. Emphasize to them that soil is often a combination of soil types.

CLAY SOIL
STICK TOGETHER
WHEN ROLLED INTO
TUBE SHAPE

LOAM SOIL
STICK TOGETHER
SOMEWHAT

SANDY SOIL
DOES NOT STICK
TOGETHER

# IT'S A DIRTY JOB BUT SOMEBODY HAS TO DO IT!

On first glance, a handful of soil might look like nothing more than dirt. But soil is really a mixture of many things. Minerals, air, water, and *organic* materials may be found in one handful of soil. The animal wastes, living remains of plants and animals, and microorganisms make up the organic portion of soil. This organic portion of the soil is called *humus*. Soil that is rich in humus is black or brown in color. It has a loose, spongy structure that helps to hold water, which is essential for plant and animal life in the soil.

People who work with soil classify it into types. Three of the most common types are *sandy soil*, *clay soil*, and *silt soil*. Sandy soil feels gritty and its particles can be seen without a microscope. Clay soil is sticky when wet. Clay particles are so small they require a microscope to see them. Silt soil has larger particles than clay, but smaller than sand. Silt feels like baby powder or talcum powder.

The size of particles in soil helps determine their water-holding ability. Sandy soil is very porous, and water passes quickly through its particles. Clay soil is sticky when wet and clings together to allow very little water to pass through its particles. Silt soil has drainage ability in between that of clay and sand.

*Loam* is the name given soil that has almost equal quantities of sand, silt, and clay. It also contains organic materials. Loam is the soil of choice for growing crops and can be purchased as potting soil. The high content of humus in loam gives it excellent water-holding abilities and also allows a moderate amount of drainage.

The water-holding capacity and the drainage capabilities of soil are very important to plant growth. Farmers and gardeners want soil to hold water and drain properly. See Table 1 for a comparison of some soil types.

## Table 1: Soil properties

| Property | Sandy soil | Clay soil | Loam soil |
|---|---|---|---|
| Drainage | Excellent | Very poor | Good |
| Water-holding capacity | Poor | Excellent | Good |
| Ability to hold nutrients | Poor | Excellent | Good |

# IT'S A DIRTY JOB BUT SOMEBODY HAS TO DO IT!

**PURPOSE:** Compare the drainage of water through different soil types.

**MATERIALS NEEDED:**

Clay
Sand
Loam
Three 12- or 16-ounce, empty plastic bottles
Cotton gauze or coffee filters
Three rubber bands
Water
A small beaker
Three graduated cylinders
Scissors
Clock

**PROCEDURE:**

1. Cut three plastic drink bottles in half. Make your cuts so that you can use the tops of the bottles as funnels and the bottoms as supports. Invert the top half of each bottle into the bottom half (see Figure 1). Label the three bottles as A, B, and C.

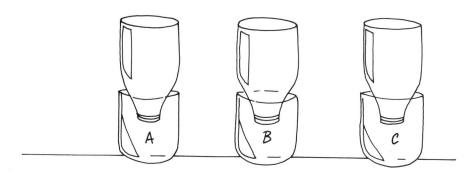

**Figure 1: Bottles prepared for lab**

2. Cover the mouth of each bottle with cotton gauze or a coffee filter held in place with a rubber band.

3. Add 100 grams of sand to Bottle A.

4. Add 100 grams of clay to Bottle B.

5. Add 100 grams of loam to Bottle C (see Figure 2).

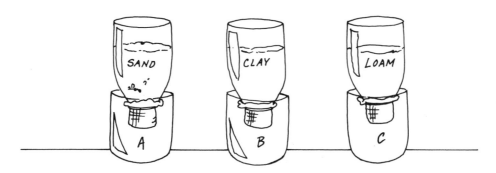

**Figure 2: Soil in bottles covered with gauze**

6. Add 100 ml of water to each bottle.

7. Record the time it takes for the first drop of water to pass through each soil sample and hit the container below. Record these times in Data Table 1.

8. Every 5 minutes for 15 minutes use the graduated cylinder to measure the amount of water that collects in each container. Record this in the Data Table.

| Soil type | Time required for first drop | ml of water after 5 minutes | ml of water after 10 minutes | ml of water after 15 minutes |
|---|---|---|---|---|
| Container A | | | | |
| Container B | | | | |
| Container C | | | | |

## CONCLUSIONS:

1. Which soil type allowed the water to pass through most quickly? _____

2. Which soil type held the water the longest? _____

3. Which soil type held water most effectively? _____

4. Which soil type is the quickest in allowing water to drain through it? _____

5. If you were a plant, which soil type would you prefer? Explain your reason.

   _____

   _____

6. If you built a house on a soil made of clay, what do you think could happen to the house after many heavy rainstorms?

   _____

   _____

7. Explain the difference between sand, clay, and loam soil.

   _____

   _____

   _____

8. Why would you not want to plant your vegetable garden in sandy soil?

   _____

   _____

   _____

# MOISTURE IN THE SOIL

**Objective:** To determine the percentage of water in several soil samples.

**Time Required:**  30 minutes on Day 1
50 to 70 minutes on Day 2

**Notes to the Teacher:**

Take four buckets and a shovel outside and collect soil from four distinctly different areas of the campus. For example, you might select soil from a flower bed, the lawn, a high traffic area, a damp or swampy area, or a ball field. After the lab, reveal to students the sources of your samples. Ask them to explain their findings in light of the places where you collected the samples. Try to help students correlate the amount of moisture in each soil sample to their general knowledge about the kinds of soil particles that made up that sample.

If it is not convenient for you to collect soil samples, assign this task to students. Give each student a Zip-loc plastic bag and have them bring a soil sample to class. Remind them to write the original location of their samples on the outside of their bags.

The amount of water that soil can hold depends on soil *porosity*, or the percentage of the soil that is pore space. Porosity depends on many factors, including soil particle shape and size. Round particles have a lot of space between them, whereas angular particles fit together better and provide less space. Porosity is greatest in soils made of an assortment of particle sizes and shapes.

Soil particles have positively and negatively charged sites. If a drop of water is added to very dry soil, it adheres to the soil and spreads across its surface. Because water molecules are polar, they are strongly attracted to soil particles. This layer of water covering soil particles is called *adhesion water*.

Adhesion water is so strongly attracted that it moves very little. It can be removed by drying in an oven. In the soil, adhesion water is generally unavailable to plants and microorganisms.

After soil particles are coated with adhesion water, additional water binds to these particles due to the attractive forces between water particles. This additional water, *cohesion water*, is slightly mobile and generally available to living things.

# MOISTURE IN THE SOIL

Water molecules are well-traveled particles. They have visited oceans, lakes, rivers, plants, and animals. Through the water cycle, water molecules travel all over the earth. Water evaporates from oceans, rivers, lakes, soils, and plants and forms clouds. From there it falls back to the earth as some form of precipitation: rain, snow, sleet, or hail. Water can fall onto bodies of surface water, such as oceans, lakes, and rivers, or it can fall onto the soil.

About 70 percent of the precipitation that falls on the earth travels through plants and soils. Some soils hold enough water to support plant and animal life, whereas other soils cannot. Soil that holds a lot of water can only support plants that are especially adapted to wet soil conditions. This type of soil is generally found in wetlands.

The amount of water that soil can hold depends on several factors. One of those factors is the amount of space between soil particles. Some soils, such as *sands* have a lot of pore space. Sand particles do not fit closely together, and they leave plenty of room for the accumulation of water. However, water travels quickly through sandy soil.

Soils can be made of small, round particles, such as *clay*. Clay particles fit closely together, and there is not much room between particles for water. Because clay particles are close together, water can barely pass through clay soils. *Silt* soil particles are larger than clay, but smaller than sand. They have some space between them, so silty soils hold some moisture. Water passes through silt more easily than it passes through clay (see Figure 1).

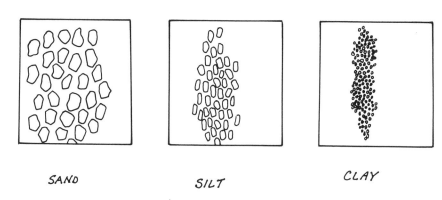

SAND          SILT          CLAY

**Figure 1: Sand, silt, and clay soil particles**

Since the amount of water in soil determines what kinds of plants can live there, the composition of soil is important. Soils containing all three types of soil particles, plus some organic matter, hold moisture and have plenty of space available for roots and microscopic animals. Organic matter includes living and dead plants and animals.

# MOISTURE IN THE SOIL

**PURPOSE:** To determine the percentage of moisture in several soil samples.

**MATERIALS NEEDED:**
Four soil samples
Paper plates
Scales
Calculators (optional)

**PROCEDURE:** **Day 1**

1. Find the mass of a paper plate, and then leave it on the scale.

2. Add 100 grams of Soil Sample A to the plate. Record the mass of the plate and soil sample in the Data Table. Set aside the plate with Soil Sample A.

3. Repeat this process with Soil Samples B, C, and D.

4. Dry the soil samples overnight under a lamp, or heat them in a 250° oven until the soil is dry.

**Day 2**

5. After drying, find the mass of Soil Sample A on its paper plate. Record this mass in the Data Table.

6. Subtract the mass of the plate to determine the mass of dry soil. Record the mass of dry soil in the Data Table.

7. Determine the amount of water in Soil Sample A by subtracting the mass of the dry soil from the original mass of the soil. Record this in the Data Table.

8. Determine the percentage of water in Soil Sample A using the following formula:

$$\% \text{ Water} = \frac{\textbf{Mass of water in Soil Sample}}{\textbf{Original mass of Soil Sample}} \times 100$$

Record this percentage in the Data Table.

9. Repeat Procedure steps 5–8 for Soil Samples B, C, and D.

## Data Table: Moisture in soil samples

| | Soil Sample A | Soil Sample B | Soil Sample C | Soil Sample D |
|---|---|---|---|---|
| 1. Mass of paper plate | | | | |
| 2. Mass of paper plate plus Soil Sample | | | | |
| 3. Mass of Soil Sample (subtract #2 from #3) | | | | |
| 4. Mass of Dry Soil and paper plate | | | | |
| 5. Mass of Dry Soil (subtract #1 from #4) | | | | |
| 6. Mass of water in Soil Sample (subtract #5 from #3) | | | | |
| 7. Percentage of water in Soil Sample (Divide #6 by #3, then multiply by 100) | | | | |

## CONCLUSIONS:

1. Summarize the water cycle.

_____

_____

2. How does the amount of moisture in soil affect plant life? Give some examples.

_____

_____

3. What are three types of soil? Briefly describe each and explain how the size of soil particles affects moisture in the soil.

_____

_____

_____

# IT'S HOT IN HERE

**Objective:** Determine how the greenhouse effect traps heat near the earth's surface.

**Time Required:** 70 minutes

**Notes to the Teacher:**

If you have 50-minute class periods, divide this activity into two parts. Prepare the three boxes on Day 1. On Day 2, have students carry the boxes outside, record their results, and answer the Conclusions questions.

If you do not have enough boxes or wide-mouth jars for every lab group to have three, require each lab group to prepare only one type of box. Allow a few minutes for students to compare data before they answer the Conclusions questions.

Earth's position in relation to the sun, as well as its layer of water vapor and carbon dioxide, provide earth's life-supporting climate. Earth's atmosphere is only 0.035% carbon dioxide. Yet, this amount is just enough to allow life to exist on Earth. Venus, which is closer to the sun, has an atmosphere that is 95% carbon dioxide. The average temperature on Venus is 457 degrees centigrade!

The greenhouse effect exists because of the nature of light. When light enters the greenhouse, it strikes plants, soil, and everything else. Some visible light is reflected, but much is absorbed. When objects absorb light, some of the light is changed to heat which is radiated into the surroundings. Heat cannot escape through glass and so is trapped within the greenhouse.

Since the beginning of the Industrial Age, people have been burning fossil fuels and producing large amounts of atmospheric carbon dioxide. Because carbon dioxide behaves like greenhouse glass, levels of carbon dioxide partially determine the surface temperature on earth. Earth has natural processes for using some atmospheric carbon dioxide. Plants take in this gas for photosynthesis, and some carbon dioxide gets trapped in deep sea sediments. However, these processes may not be enough to compensate for present-day carbon dioxide levels. Some scientists fear that an increase in atmospheric carbon dioxide will cause an increase in surface temperature. Were this to happen, weather patterns could change, causing croplands to become unusable. If surface temperatures rose enough to melt the polar ice caps, flooding of coastal areas could occur.

Other scientists feel that the increases in carbon dioxide that we have seen are not enough to raise global temperatures. Because temperature measurements in all parts of the world are not always accurate, it is difficult to determine if we have seen any global warming so far.

# IT'S HOT IN HERE

Have you ever visited a greenhouse? Many commercial nurseries raise and care for their plants in greenhouses. *Greenhouses* are large buildings that are made of glass or plastic to let plenty of light inside. Heat travels inside the greenhouse with the light. Light is reflected from surfaces in the greenhouse to the outside once again. However, heat is trapped by the glass or plastic (see Figure 1). Because heat is not reflected back out of the building, greenhouses stay very warm, even in cool weather.

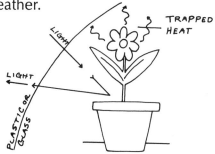

**Figure 1: Greenhouse glass traps heat inside the greenhouse.**

Some of the gases in the earth's atmosphere act like greenhouse glass. That is, they let light and heat pass through them on the way to the earth. Light striking the earth is absorbed by some objects and reflected by others. Heat traveling with the light is trapped near the surface of the earth (see Figure 2). This trapping of heat near the earth's surface is called the *greenhouse effect*. It is a normal process that has been occurring since plants and animals have been living on earth. Without the heat provided by the greenhouse effect, the earth would be too cold to support life.

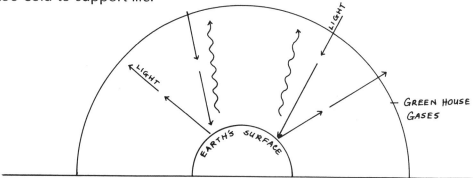

**Figure 2: Gases in the atmosphere let heat and light pass through and strike the earth. Some light is reflected back into space. The heat is trapped near the earth's surface.**

The primary gas that traps heat on the earth is carbon dioxide. Other important greenhouse gases include water vapor, nitrogen oxides, sulfur oxides, and methane. These are all gases that naturally appear in our atmosphere. However, people have increased the amount of greenhouse gases present in the atmosphere by burning fossil fuels. Levels of greenhouse gases have increased so much that some scientists worry about the earth overheating.

# IT'S HOT IN HERE

**PURPOSE:** Determine how the greenhouse effect traps heat near the earth's surface.

**MATERIALS NEEDED:**

| | |
|---|---|
| Three shoe boxes or wide mouth jars | Vinegar |
| Soil | Baking soda |
| Three thermometers | Plastic wrap |
| Modeling clay | Tape |
| Small plants (optional) | Watch or clock |
| Two small paper cups | |

**PROCEDURE:**

1. Place a small amount of soil in each shoe box. Add a few small plants to each box, if desired.

2. With a pencil, punch a small hole in one end of each shoe box. Insert a thermometer in the hole in each box.

3. Fasten the thermometers in place with a little modeling clay.
   a. Cover one of the shoe boxes with plastic wrap. Tape the edges of the plastic wrap to the box (see Figure 3). On the outside of the box, write "No Air Pollution."

   b. Do not cover the second box with plastic wrap. On the side of this box, write "No Greenhouse Gases."

   c. In the third box, place a small paper cup one-eighth full of vinegar and another small paper cup one-eighth full of baking soda. Cover this box with plastic wrap, but only tape three of the edges securely around the box. On this box write "Air Heavily Polluted with Greenhouse Gases."

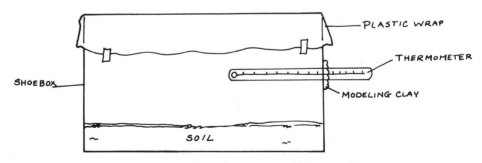

**Figure 3: Shoe box containing soil and a thermometer, covered with plastic wrap**

4. Carefully carry all three boxes outside to a sunny location. Record the temperature in each box in the Data Table. All three boxes will be allowed to sit in the sun, undisturbed, for 20 to 30 minutes.

5. When you are ready to start timing your boxes in the sun, reach into the box labeled "Air Heavily Polluted with Greenhouse Gases" and quickly pour the vinegar into the baking soda. Remove your hands and quickly finish taping the plastic wrap to the box.

**Data Table: Original temperatures inside boxes and temperatures after 30 minutes in the sun**

| Boxes | Original Temperature | Temperature After 30 Minutes in the Sun |
|---|---|---|
| #1 No Air Pollution | | |
| #2 No Greenhouse Gases | | |
| #3 Air Polluted with Greenhouse Gases | | |

6. After 30 minutes have passed, check the temperature in each box again. Try to read the temperature on each thermometer without disturbing the box or the plastic wrap.

**CONCLUSIONS:**

1. Why is it always warm in greenhouses even during cool weather?

_____

_____

2. Describe the greenhouse effect.

_____

_____

3. In the third box, you mixed baking soda and vinegar. These two compounds react to produce carbon dioxide. How did the presence of carbon dioxide in this box affect the temperature within the box?

_____

_____

# A CHIP OFF THE OLD BLOCK

**Objective:** Demonstrate chemical and physical weathering.

**Time Required:** One 50-minute period

**Notes to the Teacher:**

A good way to kick off this activity is to show students slides or photographs of the Grand Canyon. Discuss with the class how this canyon was formed. This really makes a statement about the strength of running water.

The first part of the activity requires a plastic container with a tight-fitting lid. Be certain the lids on the plastic containers you select fit snugly because students will do a good deal of shaking. Students should wear safety glasses in case a lid pops off a container. Glass containers are not recommended because of the possibility of cracking the glass. Empty margarine containers or Tupperware will work for this activity.

You may want to do a quick demonstration on oxidation for students. Place steel wool in the bottom of two test tubes. Moisten one piece of steel wool and leave the other dry. Invert both test tubes and place them in a beaker with a small amount of water in it. After a couple of days, students will see that the iron in steel wool has united with oxygen in the water to form rust. Ask students if they have ever noticed an orange or red streak on some rocks. Such streaking is caused by oxidation of the iron in these rocks.

Vinegar is recommended for mixing with the limestone, but you can get the same effect with a carbonated beverage. Vinegar gives quicker results due to its higher acidity.

This activity will show that limestone is abraded by moving water and the materials in that water. The chips will break into smaller pieces and some will flake off into the water. This is an example of physical weathering. You should see a small change in the weight of the limestone chips.

Vinegar added to limestone will cause the limestone chips to dissolve. This will be an example of chemical weathering. The vinegar will become cloudy and look powdery because it contains dissolved material. The size and mass of the limestone chips will be reduced.

# A CHIP OFF THE OLD BLOCK

Running water erodes the surface of the land in several ways:
1. Over many years, running water dissolves small portions of rock.
2. Small particles of rock carried by running water wear away the channel.
3. Pieces of rocks too large to be carried by water roll and bounce along the channel, chipping pieces of the channel (see Figure 1).

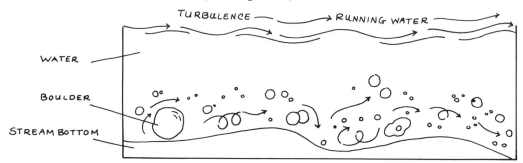

**Figure 1: Weathering and erosion due to running water**

The 1.6 kilometers deep and 29 kilometers wide Grand Canyon was formed by running water. Water moving over the surface of the earth moves soil, rock, and even boulders. The energy of moving water can reshape land. The ability of a stream to shape land and wear away rocks mainly results from energy gained as rain is concentrated in a narrow area or channel. Several centimeters of rain falling through a distance of 500 meters onto an area of 3 square kilometers gains an amount of energy equal to a small nuclear bomb.

The power generated by running water can result in *erosion* and *weathering*. *Weathering* is any process that breaks rock into smaller pieces. *Erosion* is the process that causes weathered rock to be carried away. Erosion and weathering are not only due to running water. They can also be caused by gravity, ice, or wind.

Weathering can either be physical or chemical. In physical weathering, rocks are broken into smaller pieces without changing the materials in the rock. In chemical weathering, substances in the rock are changed into other substances.

Frost and plants are two causes of physical weathering. Water entering the cracks of rocks can freeze and expand. This expansion causes the rocks to crack. The roots of plants can work their way into the cracks in rocks. As the roots grow, the rocks break apart.

The union of minerals in the rock with oxygen and/or carbon dioxide are two causes of chemical weathering. Oxygen from the air combines with minerals in a process called *oxidation.* The iron in rocks can combine with oxygen in the air to form rust just like the rust found on old nails. Carbon dioxide from the air can join with rain to form a weak acid, called *carbonic acid,* that can dissolve some minerals in the rock.

# A Chip Off the Old Block

**PURPOSE:** Demonstrate chemical and physical weathering.

**MATERIALS NEEDED:**

Limestone chips
Scale
Tough, small plastic container with lid that seals tightly
Clock
Paper towels
Wire screen that will cover the plastic container
Vinegar
Test tube with a rubber stopper
Large beaker
Safety goggles

**PROCEDURE:**

1. Obtain 150 grams of limestone chips. Answer Conclusions question 1.

2. Place the chips into a plastic container. Add enough water to the container to completely cover the chips. Place the lid on the container and make certain the fit is tight.

3. Put on your safety goggles. Vigorously shake the container for ten minutes.

4. Remove the lid and using the screen to block the chips from falling out, pour off the water into a large beaker.

5. Examine the water. Answer Conclusions question 2. Dispose of the water.

6. Empty the limestone chips onto several layers of paper towels. Examine the shapes of the chips. Answer Conclusions question 3.

7. Use paper towels to dry the chips thoroughly. It is very important to get the chips as dry as possible.

8. Weigh the dried limestone chips. You may return these chips to your teacher. Answer Conclusions questions 4 and 5.

9. Fill a test tube half full of vinegar.

10. Obtain and get the mass of two small limestone chips. Answer Conclusions question 6.

11. Place these chips in the test tube of vinegar. Observe the reaction and answer Conclusions questions 7 and 8.

12. Use your screen to block the exit of the two chips while the liquid is filtered into a beaker.

13. Observe the liquid that collects in the beaker. Answer Conclusions question 9.

14. Observe the chips that remain in the test tube. Answer Conclusions question 10.

15. Empty the chips onto a paper towel; dry them and weigh them. Answer the remaining Conclusions questions.

## CONCLUSIONS:

1. Describe the appearance of the limestone chips. Were they rough or smooth? What are their approximate sizes?

   _____

   _____

2. Describe the appearance of the liquid that remains. Is it clear or cloudy? Explain why you think it appears this way.

   _____

   _____

3. Describe the appearance of the chips. How have they changed?

   _____

   _____

4. What is the mass of the chips? Have they increased or decreased in mass from the original mass? Give an explanation for this.

   _____

   _____

   _____

5. Was the action of shaking the chips chemical or physical weathering? Explain your answer.

   _____

   _____

   _____

6. Give the weight of two limestone chips. Describe their appearance.

   _____

   _____

7. What occurs when the chips are added to the vinegar?

   _____

   _____

8. In nature, what acid affects rocks? _____

9. Describe the appearance of the liquid. How is it different from the appearance at the beginning of the activity? What caused the change?

   _____

   _____

10. Describe the appearance of the chips. How are they different from the appearance at the beginning of the activity? What caused the change?

   _____

   _____

11. How did the weight of the chips change?

   _____

   _____

12. Is the reaction between limestone and vinegar an example of chemical or physical weathering?

   _____

13. Explain what process in nature the shaking of limestone in water represents.

   _____

   _____

14. Explain what process in nature the action of vinegar on limestone represents.

   _____

# SUMMER BREEZES

**Objective:** To determine which medium changes temperature faster, soil or water.

**Time Required:** 50 minutes to set up and conduct the experiment
20 minutes to answer the Conclusions questions

**Notes to the Teacher:**
If you did not assign the experiment "Let's Mention Surface Tension," you might want to explain to students how hydrogen bonds form between water molecules. These hydrogen bonds cause water molecules to cling together until a stronger force breaks them apart. Consequently, water has some very unique characteristics.

The differences in the amount of heat needed to warm water and soil is due to water's high specific heat. Some substances require little heat to cause an increase in temperature. However, water requires a great deal of heat to increase in temperature. One gram of water requires 4.2 joules of heat to increase 1 degree centigrade. Compare this to the specific heats of several other substances:

| Substance | Specific heat |
|---|---|
| Water | 4.184 J/(g C°) |
| Ethyl alcohol | 2.452 J/(g C°) |
| Acetic acid | 2.048 J/(g C°) |
| Iron | .444 J/(g C°) |
| Gold | .129 J/(g C°) |

When heat is applied to water, much of it is used to break apart the hydrogen bonds between individual water molecules. Only after these bonds are broken, individual water molecules begin to increase their speed. Temperature is the measure of the motion of molecules.

Water's high specific heat makes it perfect for many roles. In the body, water keeps the body's temperature stable. Because the body is 50–65 percent water, there is plenty of water available to absorb heat that results from cellular processes. This is a critical role because changes in body temperature can quickly denature proteins and disable enzymes.

Water is also a good coolant in nonliving systems. Cars use water to keep engines cool, and nuclear power plants use water to cool reactors.

# SUMMER BREEZES

Many people choose to live near a body of water because of water's moderating effect on temperatures. That is, the temperatures near a body of water are never as extreme as inland temperatures. In hot weather, the air over and around a body of water remains cooler than air over land. In cold weather, the air over a body of water remains warmer than the air over land.

Homes built near large bodies of water experience another weather-related phenomenon. In the summer, the air over water is cooler than the air over nearby land masses. Cool air is more dense than warm air. Air will move from an area where it is dense to an area where it is less dense. Therefore, breezes blow from the water to the land (see Figure 1). In the winter, the reverse happens. Cool air over the land moves toward warm air over the water. Therefore, breezes blow from land toward water.

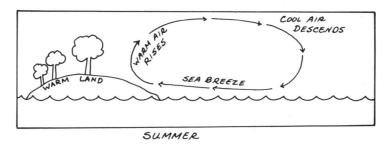

**Figure 1: In the summer, cool, dense air over the water moves toward warm, less dense air over the land.**

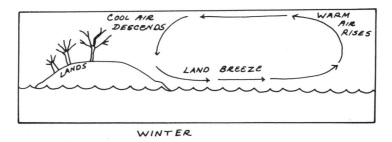

**Figure 2: In the winter, cool, dense air over the land moves toward warm, less dense air over the water.**

# Summer Breezes

**PURPOSE:** To determine which medium changes temperature faster, soil or water.

**MATERIALS NEEDED:**
> Soil
> Water
> Two 400 ml beakers or two large cups
> Two thermometers
> Graduated cylinder
> Lamp
> Ice
> Two large bowls or two or three ice chests for students to share

**PROCEDURE:**

1. Place about 200 ml of water in one beaker.

2. Place about the same amount of soil in another beaker.

3. Insert a thermometer into the contents of each beaker.

4. Read the temperature of each thermometer and record each in Data Table 1 under "Initial Temperature."

5. Place these two beakers and their contents in direct sunlight or under a lamp (see Figure 3).

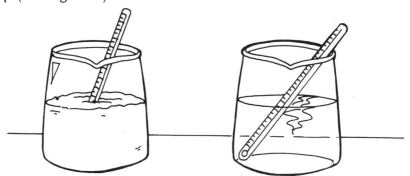

**Figure 3: The beaker of soil and the beaker of water are placed under a lamp.**

6. Check the temperature after 10 minutes and again after 20 minutes. Record these temperatures in Data Table 1.

Name _____

**Data Table 1: Temperatures of soil and water in the sun**

| | Soil | Water |
|---|---|---|
| Initial temperature | | |
| After 10 minutes | | |
| After 20 minutes | | |
| Change in temperature from the initial temperature to the temperature recorded after 30 minutes | | |

7. Fill both bowls with ice. (If your class is using several ice chests instead of bowls, omit this step.)

8. Place the beakers of soil and water in the ice.

9. After two or three minutes, read the temperature in each beaker and record in Data Table 2 under "Initial Temperatures."

10. Check the temperature after 10 minutes and again after 20 minutes. Record temperatures in Data Table 2.

**Date Table 2: Temperatures in soil and water on ice**

| | Soil | Water |
|---|---|---|
| Initial temperature | | |
| After 10 minutes | | |
| After 20 minutes | | |
| Change in temperature from the initial temperature to the temperature recorded after 30 minutes | | |

## CONCLUSIONS:

1. Which is denser, cool air or warm air? _____

2. In the summer, in what direction do breezes blow: from land to water or from water to land. Why?

   _____

   _____

3. In your home during the winter, where does the warm air tend to collect: near the ceiling or near the floor? Why?

   _____

   _____

4. In your experiment, which warmed faster, the soil or the water?  _____

5. In your experiment, which cooled faster, the soil or the water?  _____

6. When water is warmed, much of the heat energy used to warm it is required to break the bonds between water molecules. Even though these bonds are weak, they tend to hold water molecules together. These bonds are due to the force of attraction between the negative end of one water molecule and the positive end of another (see Figure 4). Molecules in the soil do not form such bonds.

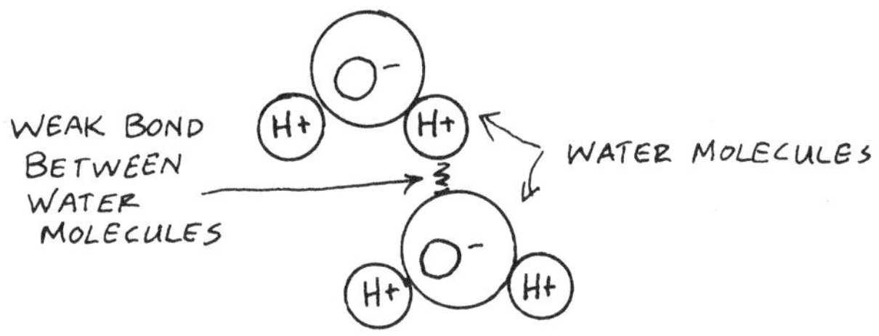

**Figure 4: Water molecules are attracted to one another.**

Using this information, can you explain why it takes more heat to warm water than it does to warm soil?

   _____

   _____

   _____

# SHAKE IT UP

**Objectives:** To examine the arrangement of the earth's crustal plates.
To design a structure that can withstand a simulated earthquake.

**Time Required:** 30 minutes to cut out the earth's plates and glue them to paper
50 minutes to design and test a quake-proof structure

**Notes to the Teacher:**
Place students in groups of two or three.

Parts A and B do not have to be done together. Part A is an introduction to crustal plates. If you use this part, ask students to find the United States and the San Andreas fault after they have assembled their puzzles. Point out that some plates are very small, while others are quite large.

Instead of supplying each student with a world map, you can display a large map in front of the room. If students have trouble comparing their completed puzzles to the world map, let them color their puzzles after they have glued all of the pieces in place.

In Part B warn students to be consistent in the way they shake their boxes when producing simulated earthquakes. To compare the integrity of their structures to the work of other students, both structures should experience quakes of about the same intensity.

During the classroom quake contest, you can shake the box to assure that all structures are exposed to the same amount of stress and strain. If none of the structures falls apart after shaking, increase the force you use to shake the box, the amount of time you shake the box, or both.

The study of the movement of earth's crustal plates is called *plate tectonics*. The crust is split along ridges, trenches, and fracture zones into seven large plates. New crust is created when plates spread apart at the mid-ocean ridge.

On the other hand, where plates come together or collide, the crust is destroyed. The edge of one plate can be forced under the edge of another plate and partially melted in the hot magma.

# SHAKE IT UP

Earthquakes are nothing new. When early humans experienced earthquakes, they did not know what caused them. Since they were not scientists, ancient people created stories to explain events such as quakes. For example, some Indian tribes believed that the earth was held up by a tortoise and that the earth shook when the animal walked. An old Japanese myth describes a giant, underground catfish that caused earthquakes by flapping around in its subterranean home.

Scientists now know that quakes are caused by movement of the earth's crust. To understand how the crust moves, think about its structure. The earth's *crust* or outermost layer is not a solid layer of soil, rock, and water surrounding the earth. The crust is actually made up of large plates that fit together like puzzle pieces. These plates float on top of the liquid magma inside the earth. *Magma* is molten, hot rock. The innermost layer of the earth, the *core,* is probably composed of metals (see Figure 1).

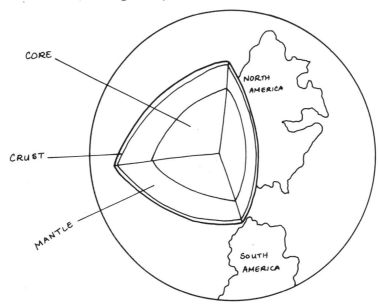

**Figure 1: The three layers of the earth are the core, the mantle, and the crust.**

The plates making up the earth's crust are not stationary. Since they can move, they sometimes bump into one another. At other times, they push past one another. Such movement of these large land masses causes earthquakes. Sometimes movement of plates causes a *fault* or crack to form in the crust. A famous fault in California, the San Andreas Fault, has resulted from two plates moving past each other in opposite directions. These two plates have slipped 360 miles. California has more earthquakes than any other state.

# SHAKE IT UP

**PURPOSE:** To examine the arrangement of the earth's crustal plates.

To design a structure that can withstand a simulated earthquake.

**MATERIALS NEEDED:**

Handout "The Earth's Major Plates"
Scissors
Tape or glue
Notebook paper
World map (optional)
Cardboard box (50 cm X 50 cm or larger)
50 miniature marshmallows
Toothpicks
Ruler
Paper plate

**PROCEDURE:**

### Part A

1. Cut out the puzzle pieces on the handout "The Earth's Major Plates."

2. Fit the pieces together; then glue them on a sheet of notebook paper. Your puzzle should look like a map of the world.

### Part B

1. Architects and engineers try to design safe, quake-resistant buildings for areas where earthquakes are common. These buildings must be strong, but flexible enough to give a little. Models are often built before the real things are constructed.

   Using toothpicks and 50 miniature marshmallows, build a model structure that is 30 centimeters tall. Build your structure on a paper plate. Design your structure so that it can withstand a simulated earthquake.

2. When you have completed your structure, place it and its supporting paper plate in a cardboard box. Give the box a moderate, 30-second shake to simulate an earthquake. Most real earthquakes last about 30 seconds.

3. If your structure falls apart during the simulated earthquake, build another one. Examine the fallen structure and decide what made it break apart. Think about ways to make it more stable before you rebuild it.

4. If your structure withstands the simulated earthquake, sketch it in the space below. Then use tape to label the structure with the names of everyone in your group so that it can be entered in a classroom quake contest.

5. In the classroom quake contest, your teacher will hold the box and shake the structures designed by you and your classmates.

# The Earth's Major Plates

The plates of the earth's crust fit together to form today's arrangement of continents and oceans. The places where two plates touch each other are areas where most faults and earthquakes occur.

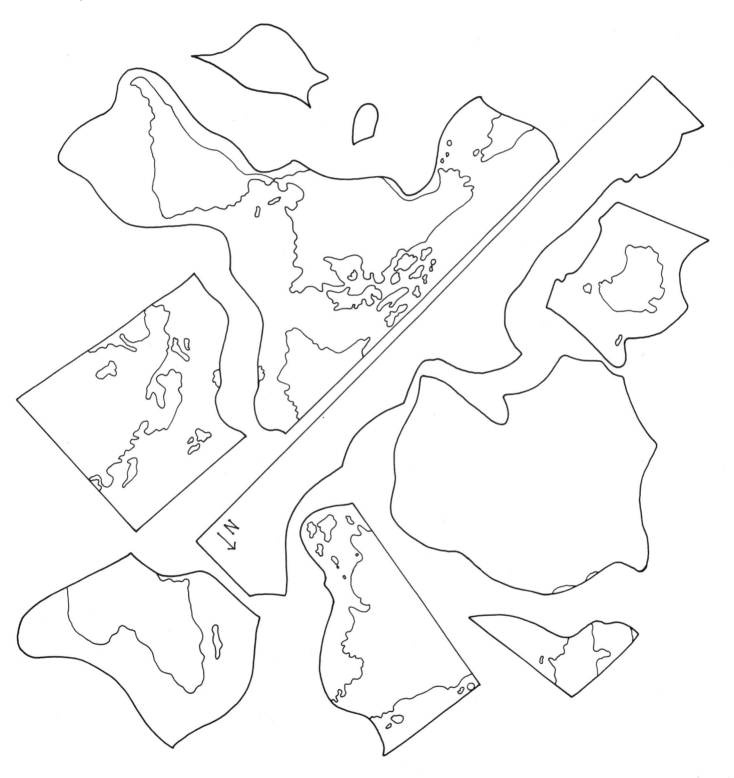

Name _____

## CONCLUSIONS:

1. After observing your classmates' structures, describe the one that was most stable during a simulated earthquake.

   _____
   _____
   _____
   _____
   _____

2. Do you think that it is possible for engineers to build quake-proof buildings? Why or why not?

   _____
   _____
   _____
   _____
   _____

3. How many toothpicks did you use for your structure? Sketch a design for a quakeproof structure using half as many toothpicks and marshmallows as you used earlier.

4. Which do you think is more stable, your original design or the one using fewer marshmallows and toothpicks? Why? _____
   _____

# ANSWER KEY

**Iodine Is Not Just for Cuts**                          **page 4**
1. Student answers will vary, either *yes* or *no*.
2. The initials are a light color. The iodine did not react with starch where the swab touched the agar. An enzyme on the swab changed starch into sugar.
3. The rest of the plate is dark because it contains starch and reacted positively with iodine.
4. If one's initials are a light color, that person has the enzyme for digesting starch in his or her mouth.
5. Answers will vary.

**Mapping the Human Tongue**                          **page 9**
1. The tip or front section of the tongue
2. Along the sides of the tongue and toward the back of the tongue
3. The tip and front sides of the tongue
4. The back of the tongue
5. Water was used to clear the mouth of tastes between tests.
6. So the subject could not determine a set pattern and guess the answers
7. So the sense of smell would not be used to help determine the answer

**Are Two Good Ears Better Than One?**                          **page 14**
Answers in Tables 1 and 2 will vary. Generally, Table 2 will have more correct answers than Table 1.
1. Two ears
2. Answers will vary. Students may respond by saying that a person who is blind develops a keen sense of hearing since the sense of sight is not available. Our brains rely on the differences in the time that sound arrives at each ear and the differences in loudness in each ear to determine the location of a sound.
3. Vibrations travel down the canal and cause the eardrum to vibrate. The vibrations of the eardrum are transmitted to bones of the middle ear. These bones relay the vibrations to the snail-shaped, *cochlea* of the inner ear. Fluid in the cochlea vibrates, and these vibrations are picked up by cells in this structure. These cells send nerve signals to the brain. The brain interprets these vibrations as sound.
4. The brain interprets the messages from nerves of the ear as sound.
5. No. Vibrations cannot be interpreted as sound without the section of the brain that does the interpreting.

**Judging from Your Reaction . . .**                          **page 19**
1. Answers will vary. The reaction rating of most students will decrease. A slowed reaction time by a driver of an automobile may cause an accident that might have otherwise been avoided if concentration had been maintained.
2. Answers will vary. The reaction rating of most students will decrease considerably. A slowed reaction time while driving may be due to looking at something else during this time. This may cause an accident that possibly could have been avoided.
3. The eyes detect a downward movement of the meter stick. Nerve impulses are sent along sensory neurons to the brain. A specific portion of the brain interprets these messages. The brain sends its interpretation down the spinal cord to the motor neurons. These neurons transmit the message to the muscles of your hand to close your fingers around the ruler.
4. Answers will vary, but may include alcohol consumption, use of drugs, lack of sleep, etc.

**Keying in on Enzymes**                          **page 24**
Answers in the Data Table will vary. You should expect to see an increase in temperature and bubbling activity in Test Tube 3.
1. Test Tube 3; bubbling and temperature increase
2. A control for comparison
3. Inactivated the enzyme; no chemical reaction occurred
4. The shape of the enzyme was altered by heat.
5. Answers will vary.
6. Hydrogen peroxide is a poisonous substance that can destroy body cells.
7. No reactions; the enzyme in liver does not react with water
8. Enzymes are still active for several weeks if the tissue is refrigerated.

**Can One Rotten Banana Spoil the Whole Bunch?**                          **page 28**
1. Answers will vary somewhat, but you can generally expect the following: Bag B will have the ripest bananas. Bag C will have the least ripe bananas. Bag D will have bananas that have ripened more than Bag A but less than Bag B.
2. Yes. Ethylene caused the green bananas to ripen more quickly.
3. Yes. Bananas in the paper bags will ripen more quickly than those in plastic bags.
4. Plastic. They would ripen more slowly.
5. Ethylene is a hormone produced as fruit ripens. It causes unripe fruit to ripen more quickly.

**A Jammin' Good Indicator**                          **page 33**
The answers in the Data Table will vary depending on the unknowns you used. If you used the ones suggested, you will find that 2, 5, 6, 8, and 9 are acids. The rest are bases. Milk is very close to neutral.
1. A substance that changes color in an acid or a base
2. a. acid b. acid c. base d. base e. acid
3. Acids taste sour, turn blue litmus paper red, and react with bases to form salts.
4. Bases taste bitter, feel slippery in water, turn red litmus paper blue, and react with acids to form salts.
5. Both test for acids and bases. Both are made from a dye of a once living thing.

**If in Doubt, Watch 'Em Sprout!**                          **page 38**
Answers in the Data Table will vary. You should expect to see germination in Cups 2 and 4.
1. Two and four
2. No. Seeds in Cup 4 germinated without light.
3. Yes. Seeds in Cup 5 failed to germinate.
4. Yes. Seeds in Cup 1 failed to germinate.
5. No. Seeds in Cup 3 did not germinate.
6. Answers will vary.
7. Capable of germination
8. Water, oxygen, and warmth
9. Once it emerges totally from the ground

**Making a Difference . . .**                          **page 42**
Answers in the Data Table will vary.
1. The line graph will vary somewhat. The line graph should show that a few individuals are very short, a few are very tall, but the majority of individuals fall in the middle of this range. Your graph should be a curved shape.
2. Most of the blades of grass are neither very short nor very tall. Most are medium height.
3. Answers will vary. Students may say that short blades are shaded from sunlight and may die or that tall blades are more susceptible to being eaten by grazing animals. Medium height individuals are more likely to survive and reproduce.
4. Yes. Answers will vary. Some possible answers include human leg length, flower color, etc.
5. Answers will vary.

## Chef for a Day
**pages 46–47**

1. Bottle 3 will have a balloon that is very inflated. Bottle 4 may show a mildly inflated balloon.
2. Carbon dioxide; fermentation of yeast using sugar
3. The yeast in Bottles 1 and 2 were killed by boiling; the yeast in Bottle 4 did not have warm temperatures that allowed the yeast to multiply, and no yeast was placed in Bottles 5 and 6.
4. Sugar and yeast; warmth
5. Carbon dioxide and alcohol
6. Answers will vary, but the students should mention yeast, sugar, and warmth.
7. They are evaporated or driven off.

## Bacteria in My Food!
**page 51**

In the Data Table, students will probably record more mold growth on the milk than on the yogurt. The milk will begin to smell sour.

1. Yogurt should be thicker than milk.
2. Yogurt is acidic, while milk is neutral. Bacteria from the commercial yogurt culture are fermenting the milk sugar, producing acid.
3. The 1/2 teaspoon of yogurt with active cultures contained bacteria that were needed to produce more yogurt.
4. The milk was cooled so that bacteria in the active cultures would not be killed.
5. After ten days, the milk showed more mold growth than the yogurt. Acids produced by bacteria in the yogurt prevented the growth of molds and other bacteria.

## It's Alive! or Is It?
**page 54–55**

Answers to these questions will vary. Grade the students for the thought processes they used in their answers.

1. Example might be a dog. Reasons include it moves, it eats, it grows as it gets older.
2. Example might be a rock. Reasons include it does not move, it never eats, it does not grow.
3. a. nonliving—requires no food, is not composed of cells, does not reproduce
   b. nonliving—not composed of cells, does not reproduce, is not adapted to environment
   c. nonliving—not composed of cells, does not reproduce, is not adapted to environment
   d. living—composed of cells, reproduces, and grows
   e. living—composed of cells, grows, and changes shape over time
4. Answers will vary. Most students will think it is alive.
5. Answers will vary.

## Any Way You Measure It
**page 59**

Answers in the Data Table will vary.

1. *Matter* is anything that takes up space and has mass.
   *Mass* refers to the amount of matter in an object.
   *Volume* is a measure of how much space matter occupies.
2. Volume can be determined in several ways: a) If the matter has measurable sides, multiply its length, width, and height. b) If the matter is a liquid, pour it in a graduated cylinder and read the volume on the side of the cylinder. c) If the matter is irregularly shaped, use the water displacement method. Add the matter to a known quantity of water, and measure the amount of water it displaces.

## A Dense Situation
**page 63**

The answers in the Data Tables will vary.

1. Salt water may be a little cloudier than fresh water.
2. Fresh water floats on top of salt water because it is less dense than salt water.
3. Rain dilutes the water and makes it less salty.
4. Because salt water is denser than fresh water, less water is displaced in salt water.

## Let's Mention Surface Tension
**pages 71–72**

Answers in the Data Table will vary. Students should be able to add more water than water plus detergent to a full cup.

1. The water appeared to form a dome.
2. The water moved as one large drop from side to side.

3. The water drops spread out quickly without forming a dome.
4. Water drops separated and ran freely attempting to spill over the sides.
5. Molecules of pure water are attracted to one another and seem to cling together, forming a dome shape. Molecules of detergent water spread out and flow freely over the surface of the wax paper.
6. Answers will vary.
7. Answers will vary, but this number should be considerably less than the prediction in number 6.
8. Water. Water molecules have a strong cohesive attraction for each other forming a skin-like condition on the surface of water. Detergent breaks the surface tension of water molecules, and the water does not appear to cling together.
9. Answers will vary, but should include information on how water molecules cling together forming a skin-like appearance on the surface of a body of water. This cohesive effect prevents small insects from sinking.
10. It breaks surface tension.
11. Yes. The pull of gravity would have more effect in a pond where surface tension is reduced by the addition of detergent.

## Monument Eaters
**page 77**

Answers in the Data Table will vary. You should expect to see iron corrode faster in test tube 1 than the other test tubes. Test tubes 7, 8, and 9 should show a slower rate of corrosion.

1. Answers will vary. Students should definitely list test tube 1.
2. Test tube 1
3. Answers will vary. Corrosion probably would have been slowed but not completely halted.
4. More. Observe test tube 1.
5. Answers will vary.
6. Electrical conductor

## Too Hard to Clean
**page 81**

In the Data Table, students will report fewer suds and more scum in Water Sample A than in Sample B.

1. Hard water contains minerals such as calcium, magnesium, and iron. These minerals interfere with the water's ability to produce suds when mixed with soap.
2. Hard water does not get things as clean as soft water. It can produce a scale or deposit on the inside of pots, heaters, and pipes.
3. Hard water can be softened by adding some detergents, by boiling, or by passing it through an ion exchanger.
4. Sample A. It produced few suds and caused the formation of scum.
5. Calgon softens water by combining with some of the dissolved minerals to produce small pieces of solid that are removed with the rinse water.

## Like Dissolves Like
**page 86**

In the Data Table, students will report that oil and water were mixed and bubbly looking immediately after shaking. However, they eventually separated into two layers. With the addition of soap, students can see bubbles or globules of oil mixed in the water layer.

1. Polar molecules have a negative charge at one end and a positive charge at the other end. Water is a polar molecule. Nonpolar molecules do not have a charge at either end. Grease and oil are made up of nonpolar molecules.
2. Soap is neither a polar or a nonpolar molecule. It has a positive charge at one end and no charge at the other end.
3. Soap can interact with both oil and water.
4. Soap gets you clean by interacting with the oil and grease on your body so that water can remove it.
5. Student answers will vary. The washing powders are basic.

## Polymer Strength
**pages 90–91**

In the Data Table, students will report the results of their tests in newtons, a measure of force. Polyester is stronger than cotton.

1. *Monomers* are individual units of long chains from which polymers are made. *Polymers* are long thin molecules made of repeating individual units. Examples of natural polymers include hair, spider web, silk, and cotton.
2. Synthetic polymers are made by joining small carbon units that were derived from petroleum.
3. Hard plastics have a rigid structure, whereas the polymers in soft plastics are free to move about one another.
4. Synthetic fibers
5. Student answers will vary. Bleach was applied to weaken fibers so that they could be tested in the classroom.
6. Student answers will vary but might include the accumulation of plastics and synthetic fibers in the environment and in landfills.
7. Classroom totals will vary.

## Geronimo! page 97
The answers in the Data Table will vary depending on the parachutes constructed. You should certainly see the fall time is shorter for the skydiver without a parachute than for the ones with a parachute. Generally the larger the parachute the greater the fall time.
1. Answers will vary.
2. The amount of compressed air increased with the size of the parachute.
3. It resists motion of the skydiver. Athletes generally do not like drag because it slows them down in their sport where speed is essential.
4. The more compressed air there is, the more fall time required.
5. Answers will vary but could include discussion of air guns or automobile tires.
6. Gravity and upward force of compressed air

## Pick It Up! page 102
Results in the Data Table will vary, depending on the amount of weights you use. Ideally, students will find that the lever which requires the least effort is one which has the load close to the fulcrum. This provides a long effort arm and reduces the amount of effort needed.
1. Simple machines make work easier by:
   a. increasing the amount of force required
   b. increasing the distance and speed an object moves
   c. transferring force from one place to another
   d. changing the direction of force
2. Increase the force
3. The fulcrum of a see saw is the middle of the plank where the see saw is attached to a support. One child acts as a force by pushing up with his/her feet. This effort moves the other child down.
4. Required more force
5. a. force—a push or pull
   b. machine—a device that uses force to provide work
   c. fulcrum—the point at which you rest a lever
   d. effort arm—the distance from the fulcrum to the effort
   e. load arm—the distance from the fulcrum to the load
   f. load—the object being moved (answers may vary somewhat)

## A Very Cool Activity page 107
Answers in the Data Table will vary depending on the insulators used in the lab. Container A will contain the most water.
1. Answers will vary but should agree with the Data Table for least ml of water collected.
2. Answers will vary but should agree with the Data Table for most ml of water collected.
3. Answers will vary but should agree with the answer in question 1. Some possible answers are packaging material, cotton, or other material with air pockets.
4. The amount of trapped air determines how well it slows the movement of heat.
5. The metal and glass inside a thermos have a partial vacuum to help reduce heat transfer.
6. A measurement of a material's ability to slow heat flow

## How Far Is a "People Year"? page 111
Answers in the Calculation section will vary based on original speed. Answers given below will be based on a runner who can run 50 meters in 10 seconds.
Calculations
1. S= 50 m/10 sec = 5 m/sec
2. 5 m/sec - 1,000 m/km = .0050 km/sec
3. .0050 km/sec x 60 sec/min = 0.3 km/min
4. 0.3 km/min x 60 min/ hr = 18 km/hr
5. 18 km/hr x 24 hr/day = 432 km/day
6. 432 km/day x 365 day/yr = 157,680 km/yr
7. Sirius is nine light years away. In one year light travels 9.46 trillion kilometers. To find your answer you would have to divide 9.46 trillion by 157,680 kilometers.
8. The sun is 150 million km away. To find out the number of "people years" you are from the sun, divide 150 million km by 157,680 km/year.
Conclusions
1. A "people year" is the distance a person could run in kilometers during a one-year period at a constant speed.
2. It takes light 25 years to travel from this star to the earth.
3. Light is much faster and it maintains constant speed.
4. They are both messengers and measure distance. Light is constant and fast.

## Distances and Diameters page 118
Answers in the Data Tables will vary based on the teacher's selection of balls.
Answers solving the equation will vary based on the data entered. Check for accuracy in setting up the equation.
1. Answers will vary. Differences could be due to different types of human error.
2. The diameter of the moon is 3,475.8 km or 3,475,800,000 cm. Human error can account for any differences.
3. Yes
4. Answers will vary but should involve the same distance-to-diameter ratios as used in the lab.

## Dinosaur Feet pages 122-123
1. A fossil is an imprint or part of an organism that lived long ago.
2. Parts of living things can be fossilized when they are covered with layers of soil. Over time, compression of organisms within these layers of soil produces sedimentary rocks and fossils.
3. Student answers may vary. The heat of igneous rock destroys the remains of once living things.
4. #6 Its footprints are covered with footprints from most other animals.
5. Animals #8 entered before #6. A footprint from #8 is partially covered with a footprint from #6.
6. The plant eaters were traveling as a group. Several large animals walked on the outside, with young animals between them. One animal, #6, led the group.
7. Animal #2 traveled through the area last. Its footprints are on top of all other prints.
8. Student answers will vary. Animal #9's tracks wander in and out among the adults' tracks. It might have been playing.
9. Animal #5 was probably older than animal #7 because its footprints are large.
10. Student answers will vary. There is no evidence of a fight; all animals seem to be traveling.

## It's a Dirty Job But Somebody Has to Do It! page 128
The answers in the Data Table will vary, but you should find that sandy soil allows the first drop to penetrate. Clay is the last to allow a drop to penetrate. Sand will allow the most milliliters of water to travel through it; clay will allow the least.
1. sand
2. clay
3. clay
4. sand

5. Loam. It has both good water holding and drainage capacity.
6. Answers will vary. You would expect erosion of the clay. The house may slide if on a hill.
7. Answers will vary.
8. Poor water-holding ability and leaching of nutrients from the soil

**Moisture in the Soil**                                    **page 132**

In the Data Table, student answers will vary considerably. You might make a mental note of the obviously dampest and driest soil samples used by the class and check the Data Tables to see if students came to the same conclusions. If you collect your soil samples several days before the lab, be certain to keep them sealed in covered buckets or plastic bags to retain their moisture.

1. Water evaporates from surface waters (ocean, lakes, streams), soil, and plants. In the sky, water forms clouds. These clouds produce precipitation, 70% of which falls back down on soils or plants.
2. The types of plants that grow in an area are partially determined by the amount of moisture available in the soil. For example, wetland plants have special adaptations for living in water-saturated soils.
3. *Sands* have a lot of pore space. Sand particles do not fit closely together, and they leave plenty of room for the accumulation of water. However, water travels quickly through sandy soil. *Clay* particles fit closely together, and there is not much room between particles for water. Water can barely pass through clay soils. *Silt* soil particles are larger than clay, but smaller than sand. They have some space between them, so silty soils hold some moisture. Water passes through silt easier than it passes through clay.

**It's Hot in Here**                                        **page 136**

Results in the Data Table will vary, but students should see the following:
a) All temperatures are the same at the beginning of the experiment. b) At the end of the experiment, the warmest temperatures are in the box containing carbon dioxide and covered with plastic wrap, the second warmest in the box covered with plastic wrap, and coolest temperature is in the box without plastic wrap.

Below is sample data you may expect for a sunny day:

| Boxes | Original Temperature | Temperature After 30 Minutes in the Sun |
|---|---|---|
| #1 No Air Pollution | 30° C | 49° C |
| #2 No Greenhouse Gases | 30° C | 39° C |
| #3 Air Polluted with Greenhouse Gases | 30° C | 54° C |

1. Greenhouses stay warm because light can enter the greenhouse through glass. Once inside, some of the light is changed to heat, which cannot escape through the greenhouse glass.
2. In the greenhouse effect, carbon dioxide and other gases in the air act like greenhouse gas by trapping heat near the earth's surface.
3. Carbon dioxide trapped additional heat in the box.

**A Chip Off the Old Block**                          **pages 140–141**

1. Answers will vary. Chips will be somewhat rough and medium in size.
2. Cloudy; contains pieces of the limestone
3. Smoother and smaller
4. Answers will vary. It should have decreased somewhat in mass. Physical weathering accounts for this change.
5. Physical; breaks down the chips into smaller pieces by action of water
6. Answers will vary. Chips will be rough and medium in size.

7. Bubbles form, some limestone dissolves.
8. Carbonic acid
9. Cloudier with some powder in bottom of beaker. Dissolved limestone caused the change.
10. Smaller and smoother caused by chemical weathering
11. Mass of chips is reduced.
12. Chemical
13. Running water over rocks
14. Carbonic acid on rocks

**Summer Breezes**                                         **page 146**

In both Data Tables, there should be a greater change in temperature in the soil than in the water.

1. Cool air
2. In the summer, breezes blow from water toward land because air over water is cooler and denser than air over land.
3. In the winter, warm air collects near the ceiling. Cool air tends to collect near the floor because cool air is denser than warm air.
4. Water
5. Water
6. Student answers may vary somewhat. It takes more heat to warm water than soil because some heat is used to break attractions (bonds) between individual water molecules.

**Shake It Up**                                             **page 150**

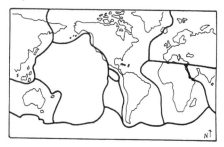

**Part A. Assembled Puzzle Pieces**
**Part B. Conclusions**                                     **Page 152**

1. Student answers will vary. There are many ways to build stable structures. Students may describe structures with a broad base and small top, structures with a large number of supporting toothpicks, and structures with a lot of marshmallows at the base.
2. Student answers will vary. It is impossible for designers to create a completely quake-proof building. However, as students' own designs have demonstrated, some structures withstand quakes better than others.
3. Designs will vary.
4. Student answers will vary, but the original design is probably the most stable. By removing components, students reduce the strength.